Handstands

EXPRESSWAYS II

Elizabeth A. Thorn
Joan M. Irwin

Acknowledgments

"Something to Think About" by Rowena Bennett. Copyright © 1968 by Rowena Bennett. Reprinted by permission of Kenneth C. Bennett.

"Mr. Moon: A Song of the Little People" by Bliss Carman. Reprinted by permission of The Canadian Publishers, McClelland and Stewart Limited, Toronto.

"The Loose Tooth" reprinted by permission of G. P. Putnam's Sons from NIGHT NOISES AND OTHER MOLE AND TROLL STORIES, text copyright © 1977 by Tony Johnston, illustrations copyright © 1977 by Cyndy Szekeres.

"splash" by sean o huigin. From WELL, YOU CAN IMAGINE. Copyright © 1983 by sean o huigin. Used by permission of Black Moss Press, Publishers.

"How Many?" from YELLOW BUTTER PURPLE JELLY RED JAM BLACK BREAD by Mary Ann Hoberman. Copyright © 1981 by Mary Ann Hoberman. Reprinted by permission of Viking, Penguin, Inc.

"Taro and the Bamboo Shoot" adapted from TARO AND THE BAMBOO SHOOT, by Masako Matsuno. Copyright © 1964 by Fuikuinkan Shoten. Reprinted by permission of Pantheon Books, A Division of Random House, Inc.

"Something Strange is Going On" adapted from SOMETHING QUEER IS GOING ON by Elizabeth Levy. Illustrated by Mordicai Gerstein. Text copyright © 1973 by Elizabeth Levy. Illustrations copyright © 1973 by Mordicai Gerstein. Reprinted by permission of Delacorte Press.

"Kate's Poem" from LOOK THROUGH MY WINDOW by Jean Little. Text copyright © 1970 by Jean Little. By permission of Harper & Row, Publishers Inc.

"Making Harpoons" by Pauloosie Atagootak. From PIK Magazine, copyright © 1975. Used by permission of the Department of Education, Government of Northwest Territories.

"Squirrel" from NORTH COUNTRY SPRING by Elizabeth Kouhi. Penumbra Press, Moonbeam, Ontario, 1980. Used by permission of the publisher.

"One, Two, Three Ah-Choo!" from ONE TWO THREE ACHOO by Marjorie N. Allen, text copyright © 1980 by Marjorie N. Allen. Reprinted by permission of Coward, McCann & Geoghegan.

"Rules" by Karla Kuskin. Poem from DOGS AND DRAGONS, TREES AND DREAMS. Copyright © 1979 by Karla Kuskin. Reprinted by permission. Pictures from ALEXANDER SOAMES: HIS POEMS. Copyright © 1962 by Karla Kuskin. Reprinted by permission of the artist.

"The Wonderful Mouse" by Karen Crossley. From CENTURY OF A CITY: A POETRY PROJECT, compiled by Professor Victor Froese, University of Manitoba. Reproduced by permission.

Design   Pronk & Associates

Cover Illustrator   Greg Ruhl

Illustrators

Scott Caple 5; Cyndy Szekeres 7-11; Alan Daniels 12-17; Alan Barnard 18-19; David Partington 23-31; Kim LaFave 32-33; David Aspenlieder 35-39; Vesna Krstanovich 40, 160; Janet Wilson 44-49, 150-152; Lissa Calvert 50-54; June Lawrason 55-59; Graham Bardell 60-69; Mordicai Gerstein 70-83; T.C. Jordison 86-95; Barb Massey 106, 129-135, 153-159; Dick Gackenbach 114-121; Ted Hill 122-128; Karla Kuskin 136-138; David Simpson 140-148

Photography

Faye E. Arends 6, 109; Information Canada Phototèque 20 (top); Province of British Columbia 20 (bottom); Saskatoon Region, Department of Tourism and Renewable Resources, Government of Saskatchewan 21 (top); New Brunswick Department of Tourism 21 (bottom); Government of British Columbia, Department of Recreation and Travel Industry 22 (top); Harold Green 22 (bottom); Hot Shots Stock Shots, Inc. 41-42, 47; Miller Services 43; Jeff Siamon 86-95; Leigh Britnell 91-105; Black Creek Pioneer Village 108-109, 111 (top), 113; The Metropolitan Toronto and Region Conservation Authority 110, 111 (bottom), 112; St. Lawrence Park Commission 109 (bottom right)

Photographs on pages 84-85 are provided by the following: Pat Norwood (Peace Tower), Manfred Petz (Terry Fox Monument), Information Canada Phototèque, and by courtesy of the provincial governments.

Canadian Cataloguing in Publication Data

Main entry under title:

Handstands

For use in grade 3.
ISBN 0-7715-6785-5

1. Readers (Primary). 2. Readers—1950-
I. Thorn, Elizabeth A., 1930-   . II. Irwin, Joan M.

PE1117.T46 1987   428.6   C86-094965-6

Copyright © 1987 Gage Educational Publishing Company
A Division of Canada Publishing Corporation
Toronto   Ontario   Canada

ISBN 0-7715-6785-5
1 2 3 4 5 6 7 8 9 AP 95 94 93 92 91 90 89 88 87
Printed and Bound in Canada

Contents

Something to Think About

BY ROWENA BENNETT

When airplanes get as thick as cars,
And people ride from earth to Mars,
Will traffic lights be made of stars?

Mr. Moon:
A Song of the Little People

BY BLISS CARMAN

O Moon, Mr. Moon,
When you comin' down?
Down on the hilltop,
Down in the glen,
Out in the clearin',
To play with little men?
Moon, Mr. Moon,
When you comin' down?

O Mr. Moon,
Hurry up along!
The reeds in the current
Are whisperin' slow;
The river's a-wimplin'
To and fro.

Hurry up along,
Or you'll miss the song!
Moon, Mr. Moon,
When you comin' down?

O Moon, Mr. Moon,
When you comin' down?
Down where the Good Folk
Dance in a ring,
Down where the Little Folk
Sing?
Moon, Mr. Moon,
When you comin' down?

THE LOOSE TOOTH

BY TONY JOHNSTON

"Mole! Mole! Mole!" cried Troll.

"What? What? *What*?" asked Mole.

"My teeth are falling out!"

"All of them?" asked Mole.

"Just one of them," said Troll. "Please glue it back for me."

"The tooth is ready to come out," said Mole. "Let's help it. We'll take it out the Old Mole Family Way."

"What way is that?" asked Troll.

"Quiet, please, Troll. I am trying to remember."

Troll was very quiet.

Mole tried hard to remember. At last he said, "I
remember. We tie one end of a string to the tooth.
We tie the other end to the bedpost. We wait. And
the tooth will come out—pop-o!"

"That way sounds bad for trolls," said Troll. "It
sounds very hurty."

"I'll sit next to you," said Mole. "And it won't hurt
a bit."

Mole tied a string to Troll's tooth.
He tied the other end to the bedpost.
He sat next to Troll. He held his hand.
They waited for the tooth to pop out.
But nothing happened.

"Hmmm," said Mole. "The Old Mole Family Way is not working."

Troll looked worried. Mole thought again.

"I know!" cried Mole. " I was mixed up. We tie the string to the doorknob. Then I slam the door. And the tooth will come right out—presto!"

"Stink-o!" said Troll. "I will not do that. That will really hurt."

"But, Troll, that is the real Old Mole Family Way. I promise it won't hurt."

"Promise crisscross applesauce?"

"Promise crisscross applesauce."

"All right, Mole," said Troll. "But I am not ready. Don't slam the door until I say 'now.' "

Mole tied the string to the doorknob.
He opened the door. He sat next to Troll.
He waited for Troll to say "now."
He waited for a long time.

"Are you ready yet?" asked Mole.

"Please don't rush me," said Troll.

So they waited some more.

A breeze came through the door.
The room got chilly.
Troll got chilly. He sneezed loudly,

"KER-SNORT!"

"Bless you," said Mole.

"Thank you," said Troll.
"That ith very nithe of you to thay."

"*Thay*?" cried Mole. "Let me see your tooth."

Mole looked. The tooth was gone.

"Troll?" asked Mole. "Did that hurt?"

"Not a bit," said Troll. "What happened?"

"You sneezed your tooth out."

Troll smiled a huge grin in the mirror. "That ith the New Troll Family Way," he said.

"That is a good way," said Mole.

"And you are a good friend," said Troll. "It really helped to have you next to me."

"Yes," said Mole. "That always helps a lot."

Then they went to look for the tooth.

Luke's Lost Tooth

BY MARY ANN JONES

It was the last day of summer holidays. It had been a great summer, filled with adventures and it seemed too good to end. All week, Luke had been making the most of every hour, knowing too well that school would start soon.

Now it was Monday, Labor Day, the last day before his first day in Grade Two. Luke felt all mixed up. . .anxious, sad, excited, nervous.

"Why do holidays have to end?" he asked his mother over and over again.

"All holidays end sometime," she'd say. "You'll feel better once you get back to school and see your old friends and make new ones and learn new things."

"I can do all that at home you know," he said. His mother smiled. She knew he was right and wished a bit too, that the holidays wouldn't end.

Luke spent the afternoon playing road hockey with the new boys across the street. He was starving when he came in for supper. His mother let him have an extra scoop of ice cream for dessert to celebrate the start of a new school year.

After supper, Luke's mother trimmed the front of his hair. The barber hadn't made it look exactly right. Then he had a long bath.

"What if I get on the wrong bus?" he asked when he was ready for bed. Luke's sister, who was in high school and who knew almost everything, got out the newspaper.

"You get on bus 254," she said. Luke was busy for the next few minutes making stick-on signs for his shirt with the number 254 on them. Just to make sure, he wrote 254 with felt marker on the inside of his right hand.

He had a glass of milk and went off reluctantly to brush his teeth and go to bed. All of a sudden there was a shriek from the bathroom.

"BLOOD!" yelled Luke. "There's blood on my toothbrush! And blood in the sink!"

His mom came running. What she saw made her smile. Luke's front tooth could wiggle so far that it almost lay flat. But it still wasn't out. "Do you want me to pull it out for you?" she asked.

"NO!" yelled Luke. "I can do it myself."

His mom glanced at the clock. "Well, off to bed then," she said.

"I'm taking the mirror to bed," Luke announced. He climbed into bed, mirror in hand. He lay on his stomach and began wiggling his tooth. It refused to come out. His brother David came to look at it.

"Oh Luke, let me pull it out," he said.

"Don't touch it!" said Luke and folded his hands and closed his eyes. "I'm sitting up all night," he said, "and waiting for it to fall out!"

"Well, Luke," said his mother, "if you get tired, lie down. I'm sure you'll wake up if it comes out." She hugged him quickly and went back to the kitchen.

"It's out!" came a shout from the bathroom a few minutes later. Before his mother had time to think, Luke was in the kitchen, tears running down his face.

"I dropped it down the drain," he cried.

This time the whole family ran to the bathroom. David
removed the sink trap but there was no sign of the tooth.
Luke stood there sobbing.

"Come on," said his mother. "We'll write a note to the tooth
fairy and explain what happened. You tell me what to write.
It's too late for you to do it on your own."
Luke dictated the letter:

Dear Tooth Fairy,

I dropped my tooth down
the drain but not on purpose. The
spit was slippery so I dropped
it while I was rinsing my mouth.
I'm sorry but you can take the
drain apart another time and
then you can have the tooth.
                    Love Lucas

Luke crawled back into bed and tucked the note under his pillow. School didn't seem to be such a big problem now that he had his tooth to worry about. In a minute or two he was fast asleep.

The next morning, Luke rolled over and felt under his pillow. The note was gone but there was nothing in its place. He sat up, more awake, and lifted his pillow right up. He could hear a faint jingle. He stuck his hand inside the pillow case.

A moment later he was in the kitchen, his hand clutching his money and a wide grin on his face. "The fairy came anyway," he said. He ate a hot muffin and had a glass of milk.

"Better get ready for school," he said and ran off to put on his new track suit. His mother laughed as she watched him skip down the steps, at least twenty minutes early, to catch the bus. She watched the bus stop and saw Luke glance down at the inside of his right hand. He smiled, waved, and got on bus 254.

splash

BY SEAN O HUIGIN

boy
did my
mum give
me a licking

she said
she would
she warned
me
that if i
got all
dirty again
i was
gonna get
it
but gee
how can
she expect
me not
to splash
through nice
spring
mud puddles
i was just
playing with
the other

guys in
the
laneway
and there was
that big
puddle
that could've
been a lake
and maybe
there was
no bottom
'cause you
couldn't
see it
not after
we ran
through
a couple
of times
and stirred
up the
mud
and maybe
there was
a sea monster
or a mud

monster
and i had
to get my
stick boat
out
and gosh
i couldn't
help slipping
and falling
and gosh

she didn't
have to
give me
a licking
right in
front of
all the
other
pups

Would You Believe that in Canada...

BY ISOBEL CORK

Would you believe that the sun shines at midnight?

During the Arctic summer, the sun never sets, and so it is daylight for twenty-four hours of every day. Because of this, the Arctic is known as the "Land of the Midnight Sun."

Would you believe that fish climb ladders?

Salmon always go back to the place where they were born to lay their eggs or to spawn. They swim across oceans and up mighty rivers to small inland streams. Swimming *up* river means they must go *up* the rapids and waterfalls. Many salmon are exhausted from jumping again and again to get up the bigger rapids. So on some rivers, like this one in the Yukon, fish ladders have been built to help the salmon.

Would you believe that people built a mountain?

It was hard to find a good ski hill on the flat prairies of Saskatchewan, so the people "built" a mountain. Thousands of loads of earth were used to build Blackstrap Mountain, about fifty kilometres southeast of Saskatoon. Skiing events for the Canadian Winter Games were held on this new mountain in 1971.

Would you believe that cars coast backwards up a hill?

That's what visitors say happens at the Magnetic Hill, near Moncton, New Brunswick—they turn off the key, and their car coasts back to the top of the hill!

Would you believe that hot water bubbles up out of the ground?

There's no need to heat the water for a hot bath when you're in Harrison Hot Springs, British Columbia. The hot water just keeps bubbling up from underground to provide relaxing baths— even in the winter!

Would you believe that there are fields made of ice?

The Columbia Icefield in the Rocky Mountains is a huge field of ice. On a warm summer day you can have a snowmobile ride on the only icefield in Canada that is south of the Arctic.

All the things described in this essay are really true!

JOEY, THE LOST KANGAROO

BY HERMIONE FREY

One beautiful day when the sky was blue and the sun was warm, a lonely little kangaroo sat all by himself, crying and crying. The tears rolled down his nose, and over his stomach, and fell—plop!—in a puddle at his funny feet.

He cried

and cried

and cried.

Along came a rabbit. "Hello," she said. "I am Rosie. Who are you?"

"I'm Joey," the kangaroo sobbed.

"What's the matter, Joey?" asked Rosie.

"I—have n-nowhere—to—live," cried Joey. "I w-wish I had somewhere to live."

"Oh, goodness me!" said Rosie. "How can I help? Let me think."

And Rosie sat down
fluffy-puffy tail

on her
to have a

big,

big,

THINK.

Then she said, "I know! I will make you a
burrow like mine!"
She hopped over to a bank of soft, brown
earth and began to dig with her paws. Soon
there was a wide, deep hole going down
under the grass.
    "There!" said Rosie. "Hop in and try that."
Joey hopped into the new burrow. He began
to cry harder than ever.
    "I—don't—like—this—house. It is too deep,"
he cried.

Suddenly a very growly voice growled,
"Ho, ho, ho! What's all this noise I hear?" And there
above the burrow stood Henry Bear.

Rosie Rabbit told Henry Bear about Joey.

Henry said,
and sat down
furry-burry seat

"Hmm,"
on his
to have a

big,

big,

THINK.

"Just the thing!" Henry exclaimed.
"Why don't you live in a tree as I do?
Safe, and comfortable, too."

Joey was still crying, but he said, "All right, Henry Bear. I'll try." Rosie and Henry pushed and heaved until they got Joey up on the first branch. There he sat, his tears splashing on Henry and Rosie. "I—don't—like—this—house," he sobbed. "It's too high."

Just then along came a tall, thin emu. "Bless my feathers!" he squawked. "Is there something wrong? I'm Alfred, and I'd be very glad to help."

"Joey has nowhere to live," explained Rosie.

"He is very upset," growled Henry. "He won't stop that terrible crying."

"Maybe I can think of something," said Alfred Emu. And he sat down on his swishy-mishy feathers to have a

big,

big,

THINK.

Soon Alfred jumped up. "Bless my feathers!" he squawked. "Just lie down here and call that home."

So Joey lay on the ground and tried to feel comfortable, but he just felt lumpy and bumpy and humpy and *horrible*.

"No-o-o," he wailed. "This is too hard. I—want—a nice—place—to—live."

Rosie and Henry and Alfred were very worried.

"Joey must have a home," said Rosie.

"Wish we knew how to stop that terrible crying," growled Henry.

"Let's think again," said Alfred.

Joey just cried.

At that moment, a little mouse popped up and said, in a squeaky voice, "Hello, everybody. I'm Olive. What's the matter?"

Rosie, Henry, and Alfred told Olive about Joey.

Then she was worried too.
She sat right down
on her whippety-lippety tail to have a

big,

big,

THINK.

28

Presently Olive squeaked, "I have an idea. Come along, Joey, and see if you'd like to share my house."

Olive led the way, with Rosie, Henry, and Alfred following closely, and Joey shuffling and weeping behind.

Soon they came to a field of wheat.

"Here we are, in you go," said Olive.

Joey obediently hopped into a cosy nest in the wheat while his friends watched anxiously. This time he cried more loudly than ever.
                          "No-o.
This house is too scratchy."

Just then they all heard an enormous noise that went THUMP! THUMP! THUMP!
It got louder and louder.

The friends were very frightened.
Joey even stopped crying. "Bless my feathers!"
said Alfred. "What can it be?" Then they heard
a voice calling "Jo-ey—Jo-eey—."

The thumping
suddenly,
before them
a big mother

stopped
and there
stood a kangaroo—
kangaroo.

"Here you are," she scolded.
"You must learn to stay home
and not go wandering."

She picked up Joey, put him into her pouch, and thump-thumped away. Joey had stopped crying. He was home.

His friends were astounded.

"Imagine anyone wanting to live in a pouch instead of a burrow," said Rosie.

"Or a tree," said Henry.

"Or on the ground," said Alfred.

"Or in a nest in a wheat field," said Olive. And they all sat down to have a

BIG

BIG

THINK.

Clouds

BY LORRIE McLAUGHLIN

You look at a cloud and what do you see?
A sailing ship?
        A dragon with wings?
                A great white bird?
                    A covered wagon?
Any number of things!

You look at a cloud, and what do you see?
A storm for tomorrow?
            Warm showers of spring?
            Clear weather ahead?
                A flurry of snow?
Any number of things!

When You Read

There are lots of things to read about in *Handstands*. Most of the stories so far have been about the world of make-believe where anything that you can imagine, can happen.

As you read the rest of the book, you will learn about some interesting things that people in Canada do; you will find out about the strange habits of some animals; you will read stories about a boy who meets a bear, and a dog who is a TV star; and you will find a lot of other stories and poems too!

When you read, it is important to think about what the author is telling you. It helps if you ask yourself questions as you read—*Could this really happen? Would I like to do that? Did I ever see an animal like the one the author describes?* Talk about the ideas with your teacher and your friends.

If the author uses a word you don't know, ask yourself:
   What is the sentence or story about?
   What word would make sense?
   What word would fit in the sentence?
   What letter does the word begin with?

When you think you know what the word is, try it out in the sentence.

The Little Angry Skunks

BY ADELAIDE LEITCH

The bear cub was roly-poly as a puff-ball, and busy as a bumblebee, and curious as could be. In the very few moons that he had *been* a bear cub, he had never, ever, met a skunk!

Let alone three.

The bear cub cocked his furry ears, and wriggled on his furry seat, and sniffed his small, wet blackberry of a nose right into the middle of them.

In all the forest, there was nothing angrier than these three little skunks.

They told each other of their angriness.

They filled the clearing in the forest with their angriness.

They stamped their small hind feet until the pads were sore.

They waved their plumy tails until they nearly shook them off.

But nothing came of it.

Nothing at all.

They were just too small.

And still the black bear cub cocked his furry ears...

And wriggled on his furry seat...

And sniffed his small, wet blackberry of a nose right into the middle of them.

And he pushed them over!

How was he to know that it is a law of the forest that
you shall *not* cock a furry ear and wriggle on a furry
seat and tease a little skunk and make it angry?

And who was there in the forest at that moment who could
tell him?

Not the Old Mother Skunk! She knew, but she was on the
other side of the clearing, hunting for mice.

Not the Old Mother Bear! She knew, but she was deep in
the woods, sniffing out a honey tree.

Not the little winds of the forest, or the talking leaves
of the poplar, or the stream that bubbled and sang.
They knew, but they also knew that the bear cub
must find out for himself.

It was a good thing that the little skunks were just
too small!

Now, when the sun had moved until it was sitting above the
tallest pine tree, the Old Mother Bear finished hunting for
honey and came back out of the
woods to look for her cub.

And when she saw him—! *Well!*
She ran with the speed of the west wind.
She galloped with the speed of light.
And she cuffed her cub on his furry ears.
She boxed him on his furry seat.
She nipped him on his small, wet blackberry nose.

She was so angry that she upset the three little skunks herself and sent them, head over heels, right into the daisies.

When she saw what she had done, she ran helter-skelter from the clearing, chasing her cub before her.

And only just in time! The Old Mother Skunk came back looking for *her* babies.

She sniffed the air.
She stamped her hind feet.
And she waved her plumy tail.

Then she peered and she sniffed and she stamped some
more. But there was nothing in the clearing now but her
own little skunks. They were picking themselves up,
shaking the daisies from their fur, and looking as ruffled as
leaves in a windstorm.

And so the Old Mother Skunk led the way back into the
forest, with the angry little skunks following her in single file.

Still telling each other of their angriness.
Still filling the clearing with their angriness.
Still stamping their small hind feet.
Still waving their plumy tails until they nearly shook
them off.

But nothing came of it.

Nothing at all.

They were just too small.

39

How Many?

BY MARY ANN HOBERMAN

A mother skunk all black and white
Leads her babies down the street
    Pitter patter
    Pitter patter
    Pitter patter
    TWENTY feet.

Off they toddle slow and steady
Making tiny twitter cries
    Flitter flutter
    Flitter flutter
    Flitter flutter
    TEN small eyes.

Nose to tail-tip in procession
Single-file the family trails
    Flippy floppy
    Flippy floppy
    Flippy floppy
    FIVE long tails.

Up the street a dog comes barking,
Sees the strangers, leaps pell-mell. . .
    Ickle pickle
    Ickle pickle
    Ickle pickle
    ONE BIG SMELL!

Animal Ways

BY SUSAN GREEN

The mountain goat: Rocky Mountain climber

The mountain goat lives on the highest slopes of the Rocky
Mountains. Its shaggy white coat protects it from the fierce
winds that blow high on the mountaintops. Its small hooves
make mountain climbing easy. In the centre of each divided
hoof is a spongy pad that helps the goat cling to the
surface of the mountain.

The mountain goat climbs up and down dangerous rocky
cliffs and walks along narrow ledges where no other
animals can go. It stays close to the steepest cliffs so that
it can run and leap from danger where no enemy can
follow. Here is an animal that is not afraid of heights!

The tree frog: the "spring peeper"

There are many different kinds of tree frogs. Some are tiny—just the length of your baby finger. Others may be as long as the span of your hand. All tree frogs have sticky "discs" at the end of their toes for clinging to trees and bushes. The discs work like suction cups.

The tree frog lives in trees near a pond. In winter it hibernates, burying itself under leaves or soil. In spring, the tree frog's singing, or peeping, can be heard a kilometre away. The male frog has a "vocal sac" of loose skin under its mouth. When it sings, this sac balloons out so that it is almost as big as the frog itself. You can often hear a tree frog's song in the woods before a spring or summer rain.

The musk-ox: the "bearded one"

Inuit call the musk-ox *oomingmak* (the bearded one).
Enemies find it almost impossible to harm the strong,
sturdy musk-ox. When threatened by danger, musk-oxen
gather together and form a circle. The big bulls, and
sometimes some of the cows, stand shoulder to shoulder,
facing outward. The calves are herded into the middle of
the ring, safely protected from danger. The attacker faces
a solid wall of powerful musk-oxen armed with sharp,
heavy horns and strong, nimble feet. The enemy usually
decides it is safer to leave the musk-oxen alone.

The Swimmer

BY MARJORIE KENDALL

Plop.

A ring of bright ripples rolled in to lap the shore where Paula was reading. She looked up, shading her eyes with one hand. The waters stilled.

Plop. Plop.

More ripples rolled to shore. This time Paula stood up. What was out there? Salmon jumping maybe?

She looked harder, squinting. A grey head bobbed on the water. A swimmer? An old man swimming out there?

Somewhere on the high ground behind her Paula could hear her brother Eddy and some other boys playing field hockey. Then "Thwack!" A stick hit the hard ball they used, and drove it right out into the cove. It landed with a smack and a splash.

The swimmer disappeared.

"You hit him!" Paula yelled up to her brother and his friends who rushed to the edge of the bank looking for their ball.

"Where'd it go, Polly?" they called.

"You drowned him! The old man!" Paula was frantic now, pointing at where she'd last seen the swimmer.

44

"What's she so upset about, Eddy?" asked the other boys, crowding around.

"I don't know," Eddy shook his head as if he hadn't heard right. "Something about someone drowning."

"But nobody swims there," they laughed. "They couldn't! It's too mucky and too cold. There's stringy weeds and stuff."

"You must have seen the ball bounce on the water before it sunk, or something," Eddy told Paula. "Yeah. . .Sure," and they all turned away.

Paula stood looking out over the water, flat now, and dark, not a ripple anywhere. "But I did see a swimmer," she said to herself. "I did!"

By the next day the boys had another ball and were setting up their nets when Paula went down to the cove.

"See any swimmers lately, Polly?" one of them teased.

Paula didn't answer. She just turned her nose up and kept walking.

Tall ferns arched over the narrow path leading down the bank, so Paula couldn't see the water until she was almost standing in it. She parted the last spray of ferns when. . . Plop. . .And there he was again! The swimmer!

It had to be a very old man. His hair was so grey. So were his bushy eyebrows and whiskers. He was wearing something that looked like a baggy brown track suit. While she watched, he floated lazily around on his back, raising his head to look at his feet, or reach down with his hands to scratch between his toes. Sometimes he'd roll over and swim quickly in circles, then turn over on his back again.

Once he flipped over so fast, and disappeared so completely, Paula thought she had imagined him after all, but he bobbed up in another spot.

This time there was something flat and stoney looking on top of his stomach. He seemed to be beating at it with his hands.

"That's a rock on his stomach! And he's banging clams open on it!" she said to herself.

And while she watched, fascinated, the swimmer broke clams open by pounding them on the rock. He popped the meat into his whiskered mouth, and tossed aside the empty shells.

"I've got to tell Eddy!" Paula scrambled back up the hill.

"Come quick! He's back!" she yelled at her brother, running right in among the players.

"Now what?" The boys held their shots.

"She says she sees the swimmer again," Eddy groaned, rolling his eyes skyward. "I'd better go with her. She must see something."

"O.K. guys," another said. "Let's all go. Maybe when we get this thing settled we can play hockey."

"See?" Paula said when they parted the last ferns at the bottom of the path. "See? There he is!"

All the boys held their breaths. There was more than one swimmer now! And they were having the grandest time! Some were grey headed, others brown. A few, carrying rocks under their arms, would dive to the bottom and come up with clams. One would steal a clam from the next swimmer and dart away with his prize, then the loser would squeal, and streak after him. Some that looked like soft brown bodied babies were curled up on their mother's stomachs and were being patted and pulled this way and that. It looked as though some were being spanked!

"There! There's the old man!" Paula pointed.

One swimmer that looked like an old man was floating on top of the water being rocked by the waves, paying no attention to all the commotion.

"It's otters. . .," one of the boys said. "The cove's full of 'em!"

"Then the swimmer isn't an old man?" Paula asked.

"No," the boy laughed. "He's a sea otter."

"This is great, Polly," said Eddy. "I've never seen so many sea otters before."

After a while, as though tired of playing, the otters all clung together around the old one and drifted out to sea with the tide.

"Polly sure has sharp eyes," Paula heard one of the boys say as they were climbing back up the hill. "I wish she was old enough to play hockey."

But Paula was happy where she was. She sat down with her book to wait for the otters to come back.

Charlie Meets a Bear

BY SUSAN HIEBERT

It was early evening, and the sun shone in Charlie Horn's eyes as he came around the bend in the road. He slowed the tractor and squinted, trying to make out what was coming toward him. It looked like a black bundle rolling down the middle of the road. Then it came closer, and he could see it clearly. A bear! A big black bear!

Charlie's hands gripped the steering wheel. He was used to seeing bears in the woods around Koostafak, but this was different. He knew that a mother bear in April could be dangerous, and this one was walking down the middle of the road as if she owned it.

Once in a while she would turn off into the ditch and then, after a minute, she would come back on to the road. Charlie couldn't figure out what the bear was doing, and he was afraid.

The road leading to his father's farm was so narrow that there was no room to pass on either side of the bear, and the tractor would get stuck for sure if Charlie turned it into the ditch. He slowed down until the tractor was only crawling and wished that his father was there to tell him what to do.

The bear was standing still now, staring at Charlie, who was so close he could see her soft eyes. When he looked into her face like that, she didn't seem mean, but when he looked at her size, he was afraid all over again. She *was* big!

The bear stood up on her hind legs, then, with a quick jump, leaped into the ditch. Whew! Charlie let out a big sigh. She was leaving. She was afraid of him.

Charlie watched the bear galloping along the ditch and was glad that she wasn't chasing him. The little farm tractor that he was driving couldn't go faster than sixteen kilometres an hour, and he was sure the bear could go faster than that if she tried.

Charlie shifted gears on the tractor and started off again, wondering what the bear would do next. There was something strange about the way she had stood in the middle of the road. Suddenly he saw her again, this time heading straight for him and the tractor, running as hard as she could.

Charlie's heart stopped—he was sure it had stopped. He felt cold and icy with fear.

The big bear skidded to a stop right in front of the tractor. She looked at Charlie only for a minute, but it seemed like an hour to him. He had never been so frightened in his life.

Suddenly, Charlie saw something in the snow behind the bear. It was a little, round, black ball of fur. A bear cub!

Now Charlie understood why the bear had been acting so strangely. She was afraid something would hurt her cub. The noisy tractor must be frightening her. Very slowly, so he wouldn't startle her, Charlie reached his hand towards the ignition key and shut off the motor. The bear growled deep in her throat. Maybe she had been growling all the time, but Charlie had not been able to hear her above the noise of the motor.

The cub was walking slowly, stopping to sniff at things as it walked along. The mother was watching Charlie. Charlie smiled at her. He did not know if the bear could tell when a person was smiling, but he hoped it would make her feel better. He wanted her to know that he wouldn't hurt her cub.

The slow-moving little bear was close to the tractor now, and Charlie saw the big bear quiver. He was frightened all over again. What if the mother still thought he was going to hurt her baby, and attacked him? With the engine switched off, he could never get away from her. But the mother bear just stood there, looking at Charlie until her baby got past the tractor, and then she followed it into the ditch.

Charlie waited until the mother bear and her cub were a long way down the road before he started up the tractor. But then he really hurried. He could hardly wait to get home and tell his mom and dad about the bear. And tomorrow he would tell all the kids in school about how he had frightened that poor bear.

Charlie remembered that the bear had frightened him too, but he decided not to tell that part.

Knocker the Gull

BY MARJORIE MORGAN

Ria lived next door to Professor Carter and often dropped in to watch him work. One day she found the professor carefully drawing a brown baby bird that was sitting on the table in front of him.

"It looks like a little chick with web feet," said Ria.

"It's a baby gull," said the professor. "It will soon lose its brown feathers and get snowy white ones. I'm drawing it for a book that I am writing about birds."

"What will you do with it when the drawing is finished?" Ria asked.

"Tomorrow I'm taking it back to the gull colony on the island," said the professor. "You can come with me if you like."

So the next day Ria and Professor Carter climbed into the professor's boat and crossed the bay to the island.

"There is the gull colony," pointed the professor.

Ria could see hundreds of gulls on the rocky shores. Above in the air, hundreds more swooped and glided on their great white wings.

"They look like white ships floating in the air," she thought.

The professor and Ria went ashore. For a moment they sat very still on a rock and watched a mother gull feeding her baby. The baby walked up to its mother and tapped a little red spot under her beak. Tap! Tap! Then it opened its mouth. Its mother fed it from her beak.

"Each gull family has its own little yard," said the professor. "The babies soon learn to stay in their own space."

"What happens if a baby goes into the wrong yard?" asked Ria.

"The other gulls may beat it to death with their wings," said Professor Carter.

"Then we better be careful to put this one back into its own yard," said Ria.

"You're right," said the professor. "It was just here that I found it." He set the baby gull down on the sand.

Up above there was a scream. "Haaaaaha Haaah!"

A white gull swooped down and started to beat the baby with her great wings. The professor chased the gull away.

"This must be the wrong yard," he said. "We can't leave the little fellow here. We'll have to take it home again."

"Maybe I can keep it," said Ria.

Her father and mother weren't too pleased but they agreed that she could keep the gull, and they helped her to build a pen for it. They put sand in the bottom of the pen and put a basin of water in it.

Ria's father was a fisherman, so it was easy for her to get fish to grind up into baby food for the chick. There was just one problem. The baby gull wouldn't eat. It wouldn't even open its mouth.

"You must eat or you'll die!" Ria told it. But the chick just stood there, mouth shut.

Then Ria remembered how the chicks at the gullery had eaten. She found the white rubber duck that she had played with when she was a baby and painted a red spot under its beak. She set it beside the baby gull.

The baby gull looked at the duck. Tap! Tap! It tapped the red spot! Swish! Its mouth flew open! Ria carefully spooned in the ground-up fish.

"It worked!" she called to her mother who had come out to watch.

"Just like knocking on a door," her mother laughed.

"That's what I'll call him," said Ria. "Knocker."

Knocker soon lost his brown baby feathers. White shining ones grew in their place. When he was ready to fly, the professor helped Ria tie a long cord to his leg and to the clothesline, to keep him from getting lost. Then Knocker swooped and glided above their heads. "Meeooo Meeooo!" he called joyfully.

Sometimes Ria took him to a pond in the meadow behind her home and tied the cord to a tree. Like a white arrow, Knocker would dive into the water and come up with a frog. "Meeooo Meeooo!" he would scream.

But a few weeks later something went wrong. Knocker didn't fly any more and he never ate much. He just stood and looked at his feet all day.

"Is he sick?" Ria asked Professor Carter.

"More likely lonely. He's lonely for gulls like himself."

"Will you help me take him back to the gull colony?" Ria asked. "I guess he's big enough to look after himself now."

The next day they set Knocker on the island. A gull called from above. "Meeooo Meeooo! Meeooo Meeooo!"

Knocker lifted his head. With a swoop of his great white wings he was off! "Meeooo Meeooo!" he called joyfully as he glided into a flock of gulls.

Taro and the Bamboo Shoot

BY MASAKO MATSUNO

Many, many years ago, a boy named Taro lived in a small village in the mountains of Japan. Thick groves of bamboo grew around it like a green wall, and cut the village off from the world beyond.

Once there had been a path to the far-off sea, but little by little the path had grown over. At last, the path disappeared entirely; nobody ever left the village; nobody had ever seen the sea.

On the day of Taro's ninth birthday, his mother said, "Taro, go and dig up a bamboo shoot. I'll make a special dish for you tonight."

Licking his lips, Taro went to the bamboo grove behind his house to dig for a small tender shoot.

He looked and looked, and at last he found a nice one.

"This is it!" he shouted and began digging around it. After a while he became very warm. He took off his coat and hung it over another shoot that had sprung up behind him.

At that very moment the shoot started growing miraculously fast—whoosh it went—taking Taro's coat with it.

"My coat!" shouted Taro.
As he jumped up to get it
the shoot grew faster still.
Up the shoot he climbed,
but the faster he climbed,
the faster it grew.

When at last he reached the
top and looked down, he was
very frightened, for he was
high up above the ground.

After a while Taro's mother
went to the bamboo grove
to look for him. She found his
straw sandals and hoe lying
on the ground!

"Taro-o-o, Taro-o-o!" she called.

"Here..." came a voice from
somewhere far above.

Then Taro's mother noticed
that the bamboo shoot beside
her was growing before her
very eyes.

"Help! Help!" she screamed
and called Taro's father.

61

Taro's father came running first and then his next-door uncle and aunt, and his next-next-door uncle and aunt, and his friends and neighbors. From far and near, all the people of the village ran to help.

"Taro-o-o!" they called.

"Here. . ." came the answer, so faint they could hardly hear it.

"Taro-o-o!" they called again. But even as they called, the bamboo shoot became taller and taller and the trunk larger and larger.

"Let us cut it down," said Taro's father. "There is nothing else to do."

But it was no use. As they chopped, the trunk got larger still. Way up high, the tip swayed in the breeze—growing taller all the time—then suddenly, the shoot decided to take a rest.

"Look!" said Taro's father. "It has stopped growing. Now is the time to chop it down.

"Taro-o-o!" his father shouted.

"Ye-e-s. . .?"

"Hold on tight. We are going to cut the bamboo shoot now. Ready?"

63

"Rea—dy!" came the voice, far, far away.

After a great deal of chopping, the trunk was cut through at last.

"Wza-za-za-za..." down it fell—down, down, down, with a terrible swooshing noise—through many trees of tall bamboo, through groves where oak trees grew, through forests of pine, through mountains high and mountains low, the whole long day—on and on and on.

And all day long, Taro held on for his life.
All through the night he fell, his fingers still with cold, and at last, when morning came, he felt a tremendous thump.

At the other end, his father and mother and uncles and aunts and friends and neighbors listened all night long to the terrible swooshing noise.

The sun rose, morning came, and at last the bamboo
shoot fell to the ground with a final crash.

Everyone rushed forward, fearing for Taro's life—through
many trees of tall bamboo, through groves where oak trees
grew, through forests of pine, through mountains high and
mountains low, they ran all day, on and on and on.

By evening, they came to a great stretch of gleaming sand.

White sand stretching to right and to left. And in front of
them, as far as they could see, a great pond.

And there on the sand lay Taro.

"Taro-o!" called his mother. "Wake up! Wake up!"

"He has fainted!" shouted his father. "Water! Water!" and he ran to the pond, scooped up a handful of water, and dashed it in Taro's face.

Taro sat up blinking.

Everyone hugged each other and cried for joy.

Taro cried too, and Taro's mother hugged him, crying all the while.

"Mother, please stop crying," said Taro. "Your tears drip into my mouth and they are awfully salty!"

"Those are not my tears," said his mother. "Those are drops of water from the pond."

"Well," said Taro, "they're awfully salty!"

"Salty pond water? How can it be?" said his next-door uncle, and he ran to the pond and took a big swallow.

"It is salty," he cried. "It must be the sea!"

"The sea? The sea that's full of fish?" asked his next-next-door uncle, tasting it too.

"And seaweed and shellfish!" said his next-door aunt and his next-next-door aunt together.

Taro and his father and mother ran to the sea and tasted the water too.

And it was salty! It really was!

"Just as my great-grandmother told me," said Taro's mother. "Beyond the high mountains and the low mountains lies the sea."

"It has been more than a hundred years since any of our villagers has travelled to the sea," said Taro's father.

"But now things are different. We can come as often as we like," said Taro's next-door uncle.

"And we'll never get lost, as long as we follow the bamboo shoot," shouted everyone.

"Show me a shellfish! Show me some seaweed! Can you really eat fish?" asked Taro.

"They say you can," said Taro's mother, "and that they are very good, too!"

"Are they really better than bamboo shoots?" asked Taro.

"Let's catch some and find out," said Taro's father and uncles.

So they made some fishing poles and climbed up on a rock and fished. Taro fished too, while the others filled their arms with shellfish and seaweed.

68

When they had gathered as much as they could carry, they started home. In twilight and in dark of night, through mountains high and mountains low, through forests of pine, through groves where oak trees grew, through many trees of tall bamboo—they walked and walked, on and on and on.

And they did not lose their way, for they followed the wonderful bamboo shoot all the way home.

The next night, everyone gathered for a huge feast in honor of Taro's birthday.

Such a feast! Fish, seaweed, shellfish, and bamboo shoots.

"A wonderful feast!" everyone said.

"The best we have ever had," added Taro's next-door uncle, "even though I swallowed a fishbone."

After that day, the people of the mountains cut a new path along the wonderful bamboo shoot and made many trips to the sea.

Taro's mother and father and uncles and aunts and neighbors busied themselves there catching fish and shellfish.

Taro and his friends helped them. But often, they paused and looked out across the wide blue sea, dreaming about the distant lands that lay—so it was said—far, far beyond.

Something Strange Is Going On

BY ELIZABETH LEVY

One day Jill came home and Fletcher wasn't there. She went outside to look around. She ran into her friend Gwen. "Hey," Jill said, "I can't find Fletcher."

Fletcher was not the kind of dog to run away. In fact, Fletcher hardly ever moved at all. Every day when Jill came home, Fletcher got up off the front steps and wagged his tail. This was exercise to Fletcher.

FLETCHER LYING ON THE FRONT STEPS

"Maybe something strange is going on," said Gwen. "Do you think somebody snatched Fletcher?" She began to tap the braces on her teeth.

"Don't be silly," said Jill. "What would somebody want Fletcher for?"

"I don't know, but it seems weird to me. We'll get to the bottom of this. I'll help you," said Gwen.

All afternoon Gwen and Jill searched for Fletcher. By nighttime Jill was really worried. When her mother came home from work, Jill told her that Fletcher was missing.

"It'll be all right," said her mother. "A dog like Fletcher can't go far. I'll call the police."

The police said that nobody had called in about a funny-looking dog named Fletcher.

At school the next day Gwen asked Jill if there was any news.

"He's been gone all night," said Jill. "He didn't come home."

As soon as school was over Jill and Gwen ran to Jill's house. Fletcher wasn't there.

"The police are not going to find Fletcher," said Gwen. "They don't even know him. We have to make a house-to-house search and ask if anybody has seen him."

"Not everybody knows what Fletcher looks like," said Jill.

"You're right!" said Gwen. "Get some paper and crayons."

Jill and Gwen each made drawings of Fletcher. Then they were ready to begin the search.

MR. HOLLANDER

The first house they came to was the Hollanders'.

"It's an awfully cute little drawing," said Mr. Hollander. "Which of you girls did it?"

"I did," said Jill. "But have you seen Fletcher?"

"How long has he been missing?" asked Mr. Hollander.

"Since yesterday," said Gwen.

"Well, don't worry. My dog goes away for days. But he comes back."

As soon as he closed the door Gwen said, "Why was he in such a hurry to tell us that his dog runs away all the time?"

"Because he does," said Jill. "He's that huge German shepherd."

"I think that man's hiding something," said Gwen.

It went on that way all day. Every place they went Gwen found something that seemed not quite right. The one thing Gwen could not find was Fletcher.

Late in the afternoon they came to a big house that belonged to Fiedler Fernbach. Mr. Fernbach was the most famous person in the neighborhood. He made television commercials.

Mr. Fernbach himself opened the door. "Hi, there," he said. "What can I do for you nice little girls?"

"My name is Jill and this is Gwen," said Jill. "My dog is lost and we're asking everybody if they've seen him."

"NOPE!" said Mr. Fernbach. "Never saw him in my life!" He started to close the door.

"But Mr. Fernbach," said Gwen, sticking her foot in the door, "you don't even know what he looks like."

"Well—er—heh—heh—," said Mr. Fernbach, turning pink.

"Here's a picture," said Jill.

"Oh," said Mr. Fernbach, hardly looking at the picture. "Just as I thought. I haven't seen him."

He shut the door with a bang!

"Now this time I'm sure," said Gwen. "I bet he's stolen Fletcher. Fernbach said he'd never seen Fletcher *before* he looked at our picture."

"So?" said Jill.

"How could he say he'd never seen Fletcher if he didn't know what Fletcher looked like?"

Jill stared at Gwen. "You know," she said, "you really *have* something!"

FIEDLER F. FERNBACH

"See!" said Gwen. "SOMETHING STRANGE IS GOING
ON!"

"Fernbach could only know what Fletcher looks like if he *has* Fletcher," said Jill. "But what would Fernbach want Fletcher for?"

"That's what we've got to find out," said Gwen. She played with her braces. "We need your mother's help."

Gwen and Jill told Jill's mother everything.

"Let me get this straight," said Jill's mother.

"Fernbach said he had never seen Fletcher before he even looked at the drawing, and Fernbach slammed the door on you?"

Gwen and Jill nodded their heads.

"Now you want me to skip work tomorrow and follow Fernbach?" asked Jill's mother.

"We want to go with you," said Jill.

"Well," said Jill's mother, "I don't know what I'll tell my boss, and I'll look silly if Fernbach catches me—but I'll do it."

The next morning they got up very early. They drove to Fernbach's house and sat where they were hidden by a big tree. Suddenly Fernbach's garage door went up. Jill's mother started her car as quietly as she could. She followed Fernbach until he stopped in front of a big building—his television studio.

"Come on," said Jill's mother. "We're going to get to the bottom of this."

Inside, a woman at the desk asked, "Can I help you?"

"These are the children for the soap commercial," said Jill's mother with a big smile.

"Go right in," said the woman pointing to a big door marked PRIVATE.

Just then they saw Fernbach go through a door at the end of the hall.

"Let's go," whispered Gwen. "It's now or NEVER!"

Gwen opened the door. It was a big room, full of movie equipment and bright lights. In the middle, with a big can of dog food by his side, lay Fletcher.

"HOW DARE YOU COME IN IN THE MIDDLE OF SHOOTING!" shouted Fernbach.

Jill ran to Fletcher, who got up and wagged his tail.

"That's the first time I've seen that dog move!" said a man with a camera.

"YOU STOLE JILL'S DOG!" yelled Gwen, pointing at Fernbach.

Fernbach got red in the face. "I just borrowed him."

"You can't borrow a dog without asking," said Jill.

FLETCHER!

"I saw him on the street," Fernbach stuttered. "He got up and followed me, and I didn't know whose dog he was."

"Mr. Fernbach," said Jill's mother, "I don't think you're telling the truth. Fletcher never follows anyone. You took Fletcher, and I want to know why."

"I'll tell you why," said the man with the camera. "Your dog is a natural for TV. I've never seen a dog lie so still. Besides he's got a nice smile. Fernbach would have had to pay you a lot of money to use your dog. That's why he took him. Boy, oh, boy—stingy Fernbach."

Fiedler Fernbach looked as if he wanted to cry.

"Please don't call the police," Fernbach whined. "I'll pay you the money. Your dog is really perfect for this commercial. He'll be famous."

Gwen and Jill and her mother went into a corner.

"I don't know whether we can prove that Fletcher didn't follow him," said Jill's mother. "I'm not sure the police can do anything."

"Maybe you should let Fernbach do the commercial and make him pay you," said Gwen.

"I really don't want to see Fernbach cry," said Jill.

"Well, do we agree?" asked Jill's mother. "We'll let him do the commercial."

"And TAKE THE MONEY!" said Gwen.

Jill's mother told Fernbach that they had decided not to call the police.

"Oh, thank you! THANK YOU! I know you'll love the way he looks in the commercial!" said Fernbach, trembling with relief.

The day the commercial was on TV, Jill and her mother took part of the money Fletcher had earned and gave a big party. All through the party, Fletcher lay on the front steps smiling. Except when the commercial was on—at that moment Fletcher was asleep.

Landmarks of Canada

How We Helped Our Mom and Dad Build a Log Cabin

BY AMY SIAMON (WITH SOME HELP FROM KATE!)

Building a log cabin isn't very hard, and it isn't very easy either. Mostly it takes a long time. It took us three years to build ours, and it still isn't really finished.

The first summer we got our red canoe. Then we went to the island where we had our land and set up camp. I'll never forget landing on the island for the first time. Dad had gone first and cleared a lot of brush so there would be room to pitch our tents, but the ground was still rocky and full of sticks and roots. Gradually, our clearing got bigger, and we dug a fire pit for cooking.

"It's called Matty Allou, the Red Canoe."

My mom and dad got a permit to cut down a hundred trees. The best kind of trees are cedar, spruce, or jackpine. We picked out our trees in a place almost 16 kilometres from the island. Dad marked each one with his axe so we could find them again.

Dad had bought a brand-new chain saw at Paul's Second-Hand Store. This is a really neat store that sells everything from canoes to comic books. We needed the chain saw to cut down the trees, and, as it turned out, for lots of other things too.

Dad would make two cuts in the tree in a V-shape, and my mom and sister and I would shout "TIMBER" when we saw it start to lean. We peeled the trees right where they landed.

We soon discovered that underneath the Jackpines grew zillions of Blueberries. You could stuff yourself with berries and never make a dent, they were so thick.

We used a special two-handled knife called a drawknife to take off a long strip of bark right down the middle of the log. Then we used hatchets and knives to peel back the bark on each side. Just like peeling an orange.

There sure were a lot of bugs in that jackpine forest. One time my father cut down a tree, and it landed right on a hornet's nest! The hornets were so mad that they chased him down the road and stung him on his face and hands. His hands puffed out just like two balloons, and he had to stop working in the bush for a few days. That gave the rest of us time to catch up on our peeling.

At the end of the first summer, we stacked all our logs at the fishing camp on the mainland so they could dry out over the winter. They made a big pile, and the logs looked really neat, all golden and shiny.

When we got tired of peeling logs we sometimes took the long strips of bark and made skirts out of them.

The next summer, Kate and I were a year older, and so were our logs. When we came back to the fishing camp, our beautiful shiny trees had turned dark and blotchy, with big cracks in them. Besides being a lot uglier, the logs were a lot lighter. The year before, my mom and dad together couldn't lift one. Now Mom and I could carry a small one ourselves. My parents were happy because it meant the logs were seasoned and ready for building.

There were more than 120 logs, all different lengths and thicknesses. Now our problem was, how to get them across a kilometre of water.

Some of our friends had come up from the city to help us, and together we figured out how to get the logs across. Here's how we did it. We drove a nail into the end of each log and tied them together into a long chain. Then we towed the chain from the mainland over to the island behind our boat.

When the logs were over at our campsite, we lined them all up like a giant-sized xylophone or a big log road. They even had different notes if you bonged them with a hammer.

At night, Dad would play the guitar. Here he is on the logs.

At the top of the log road we made another clearing in the bush. This is where our cabin would stand. Kate and I and everyone worked hard, tearing up bushes and birch saplings, and moving rocks that were in the way.

We got blisters on our blisters.

We picked the five longest and thickest logs for the foundation. When they were all laid down and notched together at the corners, they looked as if they wanted a cabin on top of them.

Dad called us his two "gophers." We had to "go-fer" this and "go-fer" that!

The next job was making the floor. Kate and I brought tools and nails to my parents. We learned all the different sizes of nails. So when someone wanted a saw or a certain nail, we knew which box to look in.

Building the cabin itself, once the floor was done, looked like building a big box. First we put up the four biggest and toughest logs for corner posts. Then we took four more long logs, called "top plates," and notched them so they fitted together and made a square on top of the corner posts. Then all we had to do was fill in the box with posts to make the walls. They have to fit together without too big a crack. Our wall logs were "nice and tight" (as people said) because my dad laid them together and ran the chain saw between them to get a perfect fit.

we had a robber in our camp. I've never seen such a brave, rude bird. His name is the Whiskey-Jack. He's a big fat bird. – No wonder he's fat!

He stuffs himself with everything he can steal from the table or the fireplace.

Besides washing dishes, Kate and I got to be pretty good campfire cooks. We could make fried eggs and toast, grilled cheese sandwiches, soup, beans and weiners, and chocolate pudding. Everything tastes really good when it's cooked over an open fire. On my dad's birthday, my mom even made him a frying-pan birthday cake!

There were only ten days left in the summer holidays by the time the walls were finished and we were ready to put the roof on. That meant we really had to rush, because we couldn't go away and leave our cabin for the winter with no roof!

Putting up the roof was almost the hardest part of the whole cabin. You have to put up the ridge pole with supports, first. Then you cut all the rafters exactly the same, with a special notch where they fit over the walls. Then my mom and dad had to hold the ridge board and the rafters at the same time and nail them together. All this time, they were standing way up high on a scaffold on top of the cabin. When they had finished nailing on the roofing boards, the only way they could get off the roof was to slide down a tree, like firefighters coming down a pole.

When the end of August came, we were really sorry to have to leave the cabin, all sealed up with plastic. It looked sad and alone.

But the third summer when we came back to the island, everything was waiting for us, exactly the same. There weren't even any holes in the plastic. A little deer mouse had got in through one of the cracks and made a nice cosy nest out of chewed up foam rubber from my mattress. There were five baby mice inside. She had the whole cabin to herself all winter—so at least it wasn't empty.

This year Kate and I were pretty busy. We could really help with finishing up the cabin and making it bug-proof. Our cabin needed windows and doors and the ends of the roof filled in. Most important, we had to seal up all the cracks between the logs. And this is where we learned about stuffing oakum. Oakum is thick oil stuff like rope. It isn't strong like rope, though; you can pull it apart with your hands. To fill up the cracks in a cabin, you pull off small pieces and stuff them into the cracks with a screwdriver.

Stuffing in oakum was the job I hated most. It was a greasy job and we had to do all the walls. That made me feel lazy.

Finally, my dad made stairs out of two logs. He cut notches in the logs with his chain saw, and nailed boards across. This makes a strong, steady staircase. We sleep upstairs under the slanty roof. We have our cookstove in and are putting up the stove pipe. It will help keep our cabin warm during the winter.

So did I! As long as it wasn't oakuming!

I enjoyed building a log cabin with my family.

Kate's Poem

BY JEAN LITTLE

When I opened my eyes this morning,
The day belonged to me.
The sky was mine and the sun,
And my feet got up dancing.
The marmalade was mine and the squares of sidewalk
And all the birds in the trees.
So I stood and I considered
Stopping the world right there,
Making today go on and on forever.
But I decided not to.
I let the world spin on and I went to school.
I almost did it, but then, I said to myself,
"Who knows what you might be missing tomorrow?"

MAKING HARPOONS

BY PAULOOSIE ATAGOOTAK

Hi!

My name is Pauloosie Atagootak, and I would like to tell you how we made harpoons for our grade 5 class here in Pond Inlet.

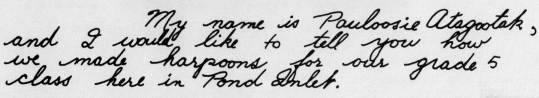

ᐊᓐᖅᑲᖅᑐᒃᒃᑯ ᐸᐅᓗᓯ ᐊᑕᒍᑦᑕᖅ, ᐊᒻᒪᓗ ᐅᖅᑲᐅᑎᒋᔭᕆᔪᖅ ᖃᓄᖅ ᓴᓇᓛᖅᑲᒃᑎᒃ ᑲᐱᐊᕐᓂᒃ ᐃᓕᓐᓂᐊᖅᑐᓄᑦ ᒍᓐᑦ 5ᖅᑲᖅᑐᓄᑦ, ᐅᐸᓂ ᒦᓇᐸᑕᑦᒍᒥ.

97

We got old hockey sticks
from the Yellowknife Public School.
First, we sanded them. Here I am
showing hiemikie how to do it.

ᐸᔪᔾ ᓕᖅᐸᒥᐦ ᐂᑭᔾᔾ ᐳ ᓴᑭᑉ ᑐ ᔪ ᖅᐳᔾᖕ ᓂᐦ
ᐊ ᑐᖅ ᑕ ᐅ ᐸ ᑉᑐ ᓂ ᐦ ᖅ ᓯ ᒧ ᐅ ᔾ ᐃ ᓕ ᓂ ᐊᖅ ᐱ ᓗ ᓕ ᓂ
ᐸᔪᔾ ᓕᖅ ᐸ ᖅ, ᒪ ᓂ ᖅᕐ ᖅ ᑐ ᒥ. ᐅ ᔾ ᐊᔾᒪ ᐊᔾ ᕐ ᖅ ᑐ ᐃ ᓂᑎ ᑐ ᖕ ᒪ
ᓂ ᒥ ᕐ ᒥ ᖅ ᖃ ᓄ ᖅ ᐱ ᔪ ᐅ ᐸ ᖕ ᒪ ᖕ ᒥ.

hevi files a notch in the
end of the hockey stick. The
notch holds the wire. The wire
will make the end strong.
I'm not in this picture.

ᓕ ᓂ ᐴ ᔾ ᔪᔾ ᓕ ᑐ ᐅ ᖅᖅ ᔾ ᔪ ᓂ ᑕ ᔾᒪ ᖅᐳᔾ
ᐊ ᐃ ᓂ. ᑕ ᕐ ᓇ ᔾ ᔪ ᑕ ᐊᑕ ᔾ ᐊ ᐧᑎ ᓕ ᔾ ᕐ ᖕ ᒪ ᑕᔾᒪ
ᓯ ᐊ ᓕ ᐅ ᔪ ᔾ, ᑕᕐ ᓇ ᓯ ᐊ ᓕ ᐅ ᔪ ᖅ
ᔾ ᕐᑦ ᔾ ᐊ ᑕ ᐅ ᓂ ᐊ ᒃ ᔾᖅ ᑕ ᔾᒪ ᐊᑎ ᖅ ᓗ ᓄ ᖅ.
ᐅ ᐊ ᓂ ᐊ ᔾ ᐱ ᒥ ᐱ ᑕ ᔾ ᖅ ᖕ ᒪ ᑐ ᖕ ᒪ.

Here I am
helping hevi.
I'm showing him
where to cut places
to grab the harpoon.
I'm awake, but
hevi looks like
he's asleep. But
he's not.

ᐅᓐᑦ ᐊᐸᕐᒃ ᐃᑲᔪᕐᑐᕐᒃ ᓴᐁᒥᒃ. ᐊᕆᖅᖅᑐᖅᑕᖅ
ᓇᐅᒃᑯ ᐊᕐᑲᑐᒍᑦ ᐳᑕᑐᐅᕙᖅᒡᒪᖕᒎᑦ ᑎᑐᕐᑉᐃᒃᖕᖕᑲᓂᒥᒃ ᑦᑦᑲᒪ
ᖃᑭᐸᐅᑦ. ᑐᐸᖕᖕᒥᒪᕐᒃᕐᒃ, ᑭᕐᐊᓂ ᓴᐁᕐᓂᒃᑐᔭᖅᑐᖅ,
ᑭᕐᐊᓂ ᔪᓂᖕᕐᑕᑐᖅ.

Steel goes in the end of the wood.
hevi is drilling the hole for the steel.
Amos makes sure it's straight.
I'm helping them by holding the
wood down still.

ᓴᐃᒃ ᑦᑦᒪ ᕐᑭᕝᒃ ᐊᑕᓗᒡ ᐃᓕᓐᓪᒍ ᓴᐁᕝ
ᐳᑕᑐᕐᑎᑐᕐ ᕠᒃᑭᑦᑐᒐ ᓴᐁᕐᒪᓗᒃ ᓴᐃᕐᒡᒍᒃ. ᐊᒪᔪ ᓇᐅᐸᕐᖅᑐᖅᑐᖅ
ᕠᐅᒃᒐᒃᕐᒍᑉᒃ ᐅ. ᐃᑲᔪᖅᑖᖅ ᑎᕐᓯᒡᒍᓪᒃ ᑦᑦᑲᕝᒃ ᕐᑭᕝᒃ.

We got steel from an old skidoo track. Koonerk and Malacai are cutting it out with a banana knife. I'm telling Koonerk he's not cutting bananas now.

ᓴᐱᕐᒥ ᐱᓕᐅᖅᑐᒍᑦ ᓰᑭᑐ ᓄᑕᐅᑦᑐᕐᒥᑐᔪ ᐃᓚᕐᖃᓂᓂᒃ. ᑯᓄᕐᖅ ᐊᕐᒪᓗ ᒪᓚᑭ ᓯᕐᒐᑕᓂᖅᑖᓪ ᐱᓕᐅᖅᒡ ᐸᑲᓂᕐᓂ ᐊᑐᖅᑕᐅᕙᖅᑐᓪ. ᐅᖅᑯᐅᑎᕆᕙ ᑯᓄᖅ ᒪᓇ ᓯᕐᒃᑎᓂᕐᒃᒥᓪᕐᒐ ᐸᑲᓂᕐ.

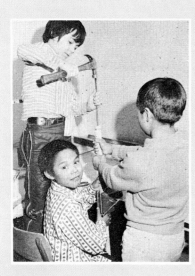

Chris is hammering the steel rod into the wood. We are helping to hold it steady.

ᒐᔅᑐ ᖃᐅᑕᐅᑐᕐᖃᑐᖅ ᑕᕐᒐᕐᓂ ᓴᐱᕐᒥᒃ ᐅᐸᕐᓂ ᖅᐸᕐᓂᒐᓪᔾ. ᐃᑲᕐᖃᑐᔪᑦ ᑎᒍᕐᒐᕐᓪᑐᑦ ᐅᐊᓗᐊᕐᓂᐊᕐᓂᒃᒥᓪᒐᓪ.

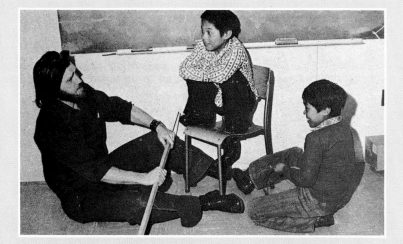

Levi is holding one end
of the wire and Leigh Brintnell is
making the wire go around and round
tight. They are pulling hard. I'm
holding the chair down and telling
Leigh to pull hard.

ᓚᕕ ᑎᒍᕐᕆᕘᖅ ᑕᕐᑕᒥᖕ ᓴᓂᐅᐅᕐᕕᒥᒃ ᐊᑕᔪᑦ ᐊᒻᒪᓗ ᓚ
ᐳᓂᓐᓅᐅ ᑕᕐᑕᒥᖕ ᓴᓂᐅᐅᕐᕕᒥᒃ ᑲᐊᓚᑎᓐᑐᕐᐊᖅ ᑕᕐᑕᒍᖕ ᖃᕐᕕᑦ
ᕝᖃᕐᑕᓂᑉ. ᓗᕐᑐᖕ ᐊᕝᑎᕐᖃᕐᑎᖕ. ᑎᒍᕐᕆᕘ ᐃᕐᕆᐊᐅᑕᕐᔪᑦ
ᐊᒻᒪᓗ ᓚ ᐅᕐᑲᐅᑎᕕᖃ ᐊᕝᑎᕐᖃᕐᑕᓗᒍ.

When the wire job is finished,
it looks like this. Now it's strong.
ᐱᐊᓂᕐᒪᑦ ᑕᒃᐊ ᐱᓂᕆᓚᑕᐅᕙᖃᑕᐅᑐ ᓴᓂᐅᐅᕐᕝᖕ ᐊᒥᖕᒪᐅᑐᕐᕝᖅ
ᒪᕐᓇ ᐱᖕᒍᓚᕐᖃᕘᖅ.

Andrew didn't put wire on his. Instead, he used a piece of pipe.

ᐊᵃᑎ ᐃᒪᔨᒡᒐᒍᖅᓕ ᓴᐱᑕᐅᔭᒥᑉ ᐱᒥᓄᑦ. ᑭᔪᐊᓂᓯ, ᐊᒐᖅᒍᖅ ᐃᓚᖁᑲᓂᑉ ᕈᔪᓕᐅᑦ.

We made a grinder and now Chris is grinding the steel to a point. I'm teaching him how to do it. It's not hard.

ᓴᓇᔪᑕ ᔨᒡᕐᑎᔨᒪᖅ ᐊᖕᒪᓗ ᑯᑎᖅ ᔨᒡᕐᑎᑕᕆᓇᔾᓂᓄ ᓴᓯᔭᒥᑉ ᓇᑎᖁᕝ ᓄᑦ. ᐊᕐᖅᑭᖅᖅᑕᕋ ᖅᓄᖅ ᐱᓴᐅᑉᔾᒪᖕᑲᑦ. ᐊᕐᖅᓇᖅᒐᒍᖅ.

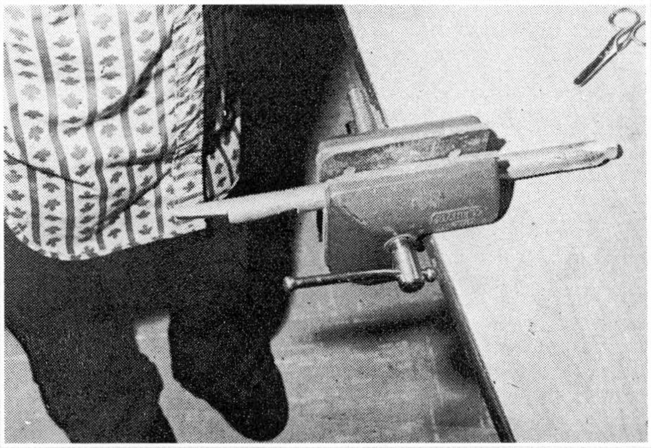

I'm starting to make my point. We call it a "sugqug." We make these from aluminum which comes from under a skidoo.

ᓴᓇᕙᓚᐊᓚᖅᑕᕋ ᓄᐳᓚᐊᕐ. ᐊᑎᖃᖅᑎᑕᕗᑦ "ᓱᕐᑯᖅ".
ᑕᒃᑯᐊ ᓴᓇᐸᒃᑕᕗᑦ ᓴᕕᖕᒥᑦ ᐱᔭᑉᑎᖕᓂᑦ ᓯᑭᑐᑉ ᐊᑎᖏᓐᓂᑦ.

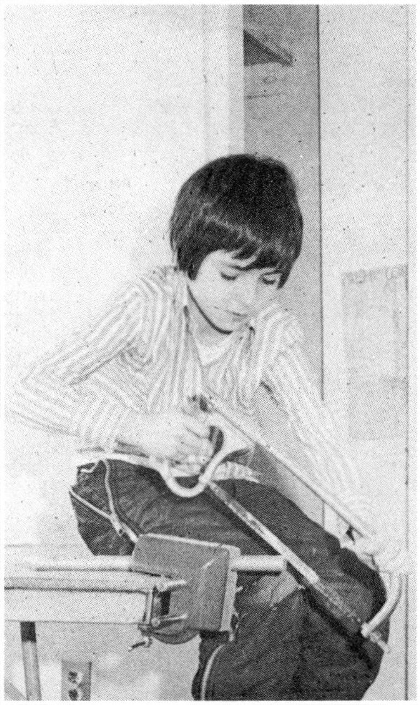

Here's Chris sawing the aluminum to make a sugqug.

ᐅᕝᕙ ᑯᕆᔅ ᐅᓗᐊᖅᓯᔭᖅ
ᑕᑉᓱᒥᖕᒐ ᓴᕕᖕᒥᒃ ᓱᒃᑯᓚᐅᕐᓂᐊᕋᒥ.

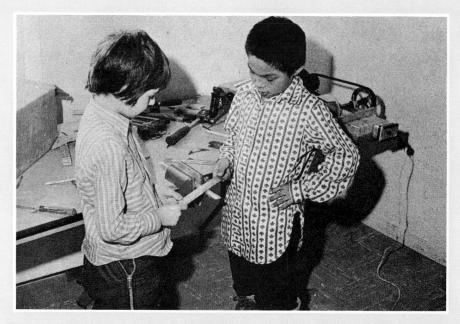

Chris and I are filing the suggug to make it smooth.

ᑯᓂᑐ ᒪᓂᕐᑫᑉᑕᐳᕐ ᑕᑕ ᕐᑯᑦᖄ ᒪᓂᕝᓂᐊᕐᒪᓕᑦ.

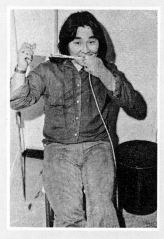

Sam Angnetsiak is our Inuttitut teacher. He's showing us how to put the rope on the suggug.

It's a strong plastic rope so we won't lose our seals.

ᓴᒥ ᐊᕐᓇᑦᓯᐊᕐᖄ ᐃᓇᖕᓂᐊᕐᖃᑎᑐᑦ ᐃᓄᐃᑦ ᐱᑦᑯᑎᔪᕐᓂᓄᑦ. ᐊᕐᕿᖅᑐᖅᑕᑎᑐᑎ ᖅᓄᖅ ᐊᕐᑐᓇᖅ ᐃᓴᓇᕐᔾᓕᒍᑎ ᕐᑯᕐᒪᑦ, ᑕᑕ ᐊᕐᑐᓇᖅ ᐱᒍᑐᖅ ᓇᑎᑉᑕᑦ ᑕᒪᐃᓇᕐᔾᒍᕐᓇᖄᓐᑎ.

Here's little me again—teaching my pal Chris the special Inuttitut names for the line and point.

That's my story, and that's all I have to say for now.

Your friend,

Pauloosie Atagootak

P.S. I'll let you know later about how many seals I get with my new harpoon!

ᐅᕝᕕ ᐅᐸᖅᑯᑯᓄᓂᖏᒥᕿᐊᖅ—ᐊᒡᖓᖅᖃᑐᐋᐊᕿᖅ ᐃᓕᓘᓂᖅ ᑯᓂᕐᒥᖅ ᑗᖅᑲᐅ ᐃᓅᖃᑎᑎ ᐊᑎᓐᕆᓂᐅᖅ.

ᑕᖅᕙ ᐅᓄᖅᑲᖅ, ᐊᒻᒪᑐ ᑕᖅᕿᔪᑕᖅ ᒪᐋ ᐅᖅᑲᐅᕆᓂᐊᕿᑕᖅ.
ᐃᓕ ᐊᐃ,
ᐸᐅᓘᓯ ᐊᑕᒍᑕᖅ

ᐅᖅᑲᐅᕆᓚᖅᕙᓯ ᖅᑯᑦᑐᑐᐃᐊᓇᐅᑎᓕᖅᕙᖏ ᖃᖅᕿᓂᖅ ᐊᓐᑎᓇᐅᖅᒪᕐᓇᒪᖅ ᑕᖅᑯᓪᕿ ᓴᓇᓕᐅᖅᖃᖅᑕᓐᓄᖅ.

Squirrel

BY ELIZABETH KOUHI

What a silly
You are
Standing there
On your branch
Rubbing
Your tummy
Nagging and
Scolding,
Making
The woods
Echo
With your
Yammer.

In the city...

My friend asked me, "What is it like in the city?"

I said, "It is noisy in the city. The cars hum and make big loud noises. The people talk and sing, whistle and yell and scream!"

My friend said, "Do you like it in the city?"

I said, "It's okay, I guess. Sometimes it's too noisy."

Lulu Gagnon, Grade Two

I hear cars humming.

people chattering.

I hear all kinds of noise in the city.

people mowing their lawns.

children yelling on our street.

birds chirping.

I make lots of noise too.

Karen Sorenson, Grade Two

Pioneer Village

BY ANN IRWIN

Suppose you had been born over a hundred years ago.
What do you think it would have been like growing up
then? It's hard for us to imagine!

"Pioneer villages" have been set up in many places to
show us how people lived in our country long ago.

Black Creek Pioneer Village is in southern Ontario. These
pictures show us what it is like. Visitors can see people
living and working exactly as the people did who lived here
long ago.

There were no bake shops
in those days.
Women made bread dough,
kneaded it, shaped
it into loaves. . .

and baked the loaves
—perhaps in an outdoor oven.
They churned the cream
to make butter too.

Flour for the bread was made from grain the pioneers grew. The grain was taken to the mill where it was ground by millstones.

In this picture the millstones are inside the round wooden case.

The first pioneers had no lamps, so they used candles. To make candles, a wick was dipped many times into hot, melted wax. The wax-covered wick was then hung up to cool and harden.

The schoolhouse looked like this. Pupils in all the grades studied in the same one room and had the same teacher.

People used brooms to sweep their houses and buildings clean. The brooms were made from lengths of straw.

Pioneers raised sheep for their wool. Every spring they cut off the sheep's heavy wool coat. This is called "shearing" the sheep.

The wool was spun into yarn and then woven into cloth.

People walked, or travelled
by horse and buggy.

The blacksmith was kept
busy putting iron shoes
on the horses.

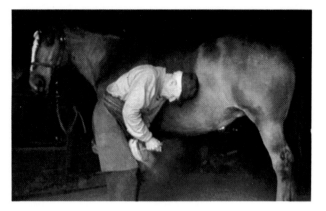

The pictures in this essay show what life was like long ago
in one Canadian village. Perhaps there is a pioneer village
near your home that you can visit.

One, Two, Three Ah-choo!

BY MARJORIE ALLEN

Wally Springer had a problem. Dust and feathers made him sneeze, and now he had just found out his puppy made him sneeze, too.

"The doctor says you are allergic to animal fur," said his mother. "I'm afraid the puppy must go back to the pet store."

Wally gave his dog one last hug. Ah-choo! Ah-choo! Ah-choo!

"Why me?" he groaned, as he rubbed his puffy eyes and sniffed loudly. "Other people can have dogs or cats or hamsters or parakeets. But not me. I'm allergic to pets."

"Not all pets have fur and feathers," said his mother. "We'll just have to find one that won't make you sneeze."

The next day Wally stared at four tadpoles that wiggled and swam inside a fishbowl. "Tadpoles," he said "are boring."

"Just wait," said his mother.

Wally waited. At least tadpoles didn't make him sneeze. After a few weeks the tadpoles began to sprout legs. Their tails became shorter, and they changed color. Soon they were frogs.

"I can't stand it," said Wally's father a few days later. "They sing all night long, and they sound like fingernails scratching a chalkboard." Wally didn't like the noise either; the frogs kept him awake the whole night.

"Your frogs keep jumping out of their bowl," said Wally's mother. "This morning one got into my cold cream." He knew what his mother meant. Two frogs had jumped into the middle of his giant jigsaw puzzle, scattering the pieces everywhere.

Wally found a home for his frogs in an outdoor lily pond,
and there he picked up a beautiful creamy white snake with
dark bands. "I'll call you Sheila," Wally said proudly, as she
wrapped herself around his arm. He fed her live insects,
and sometimes he took her outside to find her own food.
She liked Wally and always came back to him.

When winter came, he took Sheila out of her terrarium and put her in a cloth bag in the refrigerator.

"A snake in my refrigerator!" his mother cried.

"It's all right," said Wally reassuringly. "She's way in the back. She'll hibernate all winter, and you'll forget she's there."

Wally was right. Everyone forgot about Sheila until Christmas, when Aunt Beulah came to visit. "Ah—sausage!" she exclaimed, spying the bag at the back of the refrigerator. She pulled it out and set it on the counter. "I'll have a snack before dinner."

Soon Sheila warmed up, and just as Aunt Beulah picked up the bag, the snake began to move. Aunt Beulah screamed and dropped Sheila.

"No snakes in the refrigerator," said Wally's mother.

Wally knew he couldn't keep Sheila, so he called the pet store and explained his problem.

"I have an idea," said the store manager. "Send me your snake, and I will send you a new pet."

Wally put Sheila in a box, and his father took her to the pet store. Wally couldn't go, because pet stores made him sneeze. When his father came back, he handed Wally a white seashell with grey stripes.

"A seashell?" Wally asked. He put it on the table, and the seashell skittered. "It's alive!" Wally exclaimed.

"It's a hermit crab," said his father.

Wally called his hermit crab Harold. He fed him potato chips and cake crumbs.

"Junk food!" said his mother.

"He also likes lettuce and carrots," said Wally. "Besides, he only eats once every two months."

"Well. . .all right," she said. "But I think he's beginning to outgrow his shell. He sticks out the front."

Wally had a collection of shells, and he put them in the terrarium, so Harold could pick a larger one and move right in.

The next morning Wally hurried downstairs to see which shell Harold had chosen. But Harold was still trying to decide. He pulled himself out of a pink striped shell. Using his large front claws, he skittered to another shell. It was too small. He tried another. That one was too big.

Finally Harold found a shell he liked and settled into it. Wally scooped him into his pocket and ran to the park to show Harold to his friends.

"A seashell that walks!" they cried. "What an unusual pet."

Wally thought so, too. Hermit crabs were fun. And Harold didn't make him sneeze once.

The Runaway Snowblower

BY CLARIBEL GESNER

Thwack! The snowball hit the girl right between the shoulder blades and sprayed snow across the back of her red jacket. Janet Murray straightened up quickly, her eyes flashing. But she grinned when she saw the two girls laughing at her from the sidewalk, and stuck her snow shovel in the bank.

Franca Macri and Julia Kostyk were Janet's best friends, and the three of them usually spent Saturday afternoons together just having a good time.

But today, Janet still had work to do. Instead of getting up when her mother called her, she had rolled over for another nap. Now it was one o'clock, and she was only half finished shovelling the snow in the driveway. Her father had warned her to finish it before she went off with her friends.

"Coming to the show?" called Franca.

Janet pointed at the snow drift in front of the garage doors, and called back, "I don't know if I can make it. I've got to do the walks, and there's all this to finish. Maybe, if I hurry..."

"Too bad," said Franca. "But it looks to me like you've got hours of work yet. Anyway, if you finish in time, come on down. We'll be there. Bye!" And the two girls went off down the street without Janet.

Janet made a snowball and threw it after her friends, then ducked, as they threw some back. When the rain of snowballs stopped, she went back to work. She did wish she could go to the show but she knew that Franca was right. She wouldn't finish for hours!

As she went back to her shovelling, Janet thought about the snowblower standing in the corner of the garage. She had been thinking about that shiny red snowblower off and on ever since she'd started to shovel.

It belonged on her grandfather's farm and had been sent into town to get fixed. Tomorrow, Janet and her father were going to return it. But now it just stood there in the garage, doing nothing.

"I could do the walks in no time with that," thought Janet, "and then it wouldn't take long to finish the driveway."

But her father had been very firm that morning. "Don't touch that blower, Janet," he'd said. "It can be very dangerous unless you know how to run it. And it's far too powerful for you to manage."

Janet sighed, and pushed her shovel into the snow; then slowly she lifted it. It was surprising how much heavier it felt now than when she had started. She went into the garage and looked at the snowblower, and it seemed to wink at her.

"I used the power mower all summer," Janet thought, "and nothing ever happened. The snowblower can't be any harder to run. It won't hurt to use it just this once if I'm careful. Shovelling's so slow."

She stuck her shovel into the snowbank and brought the snowblower out of the garage. She flipped the switch— and suddenly the blower came to life and started for the sidewalk, dragging Janet with it.

"Hey, wait!" yelled Janet. "Not *that* way. . .*this* way."

But the snowblower didn't seem to hear, or if it heard, it didn't care. It rushed down the walk, throwing snow off to one side in a great cloud.

It roared across the street and went up Mrs. Maloney's lawn just as she opened her front door. Snow gushed from the snowblower through the open door and down Mrs. Maloney's front hall.

"What . . . ," started Mrs. Maloney, but whatever she was going to say was cut off by the stream of snow that struck her as Janet and the snowblower whizzed past.

Across Mrs. Maloney's lawn they went, into Mrs. Fine's backyard, and under the clothesline where she was hanging out the wash.

"Help!" yelled Janet, plunging past the clothes prop and knocking it down. As the clothes prop fell, so did the line of clothes.

"Stop!" screamed Mrs. Fine. Then her voice was muffled by the sheet that dropped over her head.

But Janet couldn't stop! Wearing a scarf of red leotards, dragged from Mrs. Fine's clothesline, she sped out of the yard. The snowblower chewed its way through the banks that lined the Fines' driveway, throwing snow back onto the walk that Mr. Fine had shovelled that morning.

On to the sidewalk went Janet and the snowblower, taking the corner of the Fines' fence with them, just in time to meet the letter carrier.

"Look out!" shouted Janet. . .but too late!

Janet's shoulder bumped the letter carrier and knocked her off balance. Her mail bag flew in one direction and her feet in another as Janet sped on.

The snowblower took to the street again, and Janet's heart thumped as she saw an automobile coming toward her, horn blasting madly.

Just as Janet was sure they would crash head on, the car swerved to one side and buried its nose in the snowbank. The snowblower went around the corner with Janet desperately clutching its handle.

"Stop!" called the traffic officer at the corner.

"Help!" shouted Janet. She was sorry she couldn't do as the officer ordered, but the snowblower wasn't stopping for anything, not even a traffic officer.

It climbed the curb and careened along the sidewalk, scattering Saturday shoppers as it went, until at last it hit the huge snowbank at the back of the service station lot.

Even the snowblower couldn't chew its way through that.
With a last wheeze, it turned over on its side and stopped.
People rushed from the service station, shoppers ran from
Main Street, and the police officer hurried over.

Janet sat up and brushed the snow from her eyes.

"Are you hurt?" someone asked anxiously.

"No-o-o-o!" answered Janet, shakily.

Somebody helped her to her feet and brushed the snow off her clothes while somebody else set the snowblower upright again.

"That'll have to go to the repair shop," said a man.

"Ohhh, no!" groaned Janet.

Late that afternoon, Janet was still shovelling the walk in front of her house when Franca and Julia stopped by the gate on their way home from the movie.

"How come you're still shovelling, Janet?" asked Julia. "We thought you'd be through long ago. We waited for you until the show started."

"Oh gosh," groaned Janet. "First I had to help the letter carrier pick up the letters, then I had to set up Mrs. Fine's clothesline and shovel her walk where the blower threw snow all over it. Tomorrow I have to help her mend the fence, and all next week I'll have to shovel walks to help pay for fixing the snowblower.

"And," she added, turning back to the shovelling, "I have to finish this walk before I get any dinner if it takes all night. My father said so."

Grimly, Janet lifted another shovelful of snow.

A Saturday Spin

BY SHARON SIAMON

It was Saturday, and every Saturday the Bergman family washed their clothes at the laundromat. It wasn't much fun, but it was one of the things that had to be done.

Every Saturday, Mrs. Bergman started by gathering all the towels from the bathroom and the sheets from the bedrooms. Mr. Bergman checked his work pants to see that nothing was left in the pockets. Inge and Hans Bergman had to wiggle under their beds to dig out all the dirty clothes that had fallen down during the week.

By ten o'clock, the Bergmans had all their laundry stuffed in two enormous garbage bags, and they had their big box of soap and their bottle of bleach stacked in the front hall. Then Hans took the bleach, Inge took the soap, and Mr. and Mrs. Bergman took the bags of dirty clothes to the car.

Hans and Inge didn't mind going to the laundromat. It was on the busiest street in the neighborhood, so, while their parents washed the clothes, there were lots of things to see and do. But this Saturday, as soon as they stepped inside, they knew it was going to be different. Instead of rows of shiny white machines with their lids up, all the lids were down, and the laundromat was full of people.

Children, babies, women, men—it looked like the whole neighborhood was washing its clothes. The noise was terrible. The washers rattled and churned, the dryers whirred and clanged, and the babies cried.

Mr. King, the man who worked in the laundromat, came up to the Bergmans. "Sorry, folks, we're all full," he said. "Don't know what's happened this morning. Everybody's washing today."

"What will we do?" asked Mr. Bergman. "Everything
we own is in those bags—dirty."

"Well, we can't stay here all day," said Mrs. Bergman.

Hans agreed with his mother. He didn't feel like hanging
around a crowded laundromat all day either. Already a
baby was tugging at the bottle of bleach under his arm.
Hans jerked the bottle away, and the baby sat down suddenly.
It started to cry.

"Oh dear!" said Mrs. Bergman. "Be careful, Hans."

Just then, Mr. King waved at them from the back of the laundromat. A machine was empty, so they could get started. Mr. Bergman picked up one of the bags and began to push his way toward the washer. Mrs. Bergman followed with the soap, picking her way around the laundry baskets and small children on the floor.

Hans and Inge went outside and walked up and down, watching the traffic and looking in store windows. Inge bought a pear at the corner fruit market, and Hans found a terrific set of monster teeth in the Variety Store. He hurried back to the laundromat to show them to his mother.

That place was busier and noisier than ever. Hans and Inge saw their mother, stuffing clothes into a dryer. She called to them to come and help.

"Your father's gone to get the tires on the car changed," she said, "and I'm all out of quarters, so I have to go to a store to get some change."

Hans decided that this was not a good time to show his mother his monster teeth.

"We just have one load left to do," said his mother. "If you find an empty washer while I'm out, put these clothes in—and don't forget the soap!" She hurried off to get some change.

Inge and Hans watched the red lights on the washers to see if any were finished. Finally, they saw a tall man taking his clothes out of a machine near the front of the laundromat.

"Quick, Hans, bring the bag," cried Inge.

A woman was heading for the same machine with a basket of clothes, but Hans and Inge were too fast for her. She stood there, frowning angrily, as they dumped in their clothes and slammed down the lid!

They waited, but nothing happened—the red light didn't go on, and water wasn't running into the machine. Inge twisted all the buttons at the top while the woman stood and glared at them.

"What do we do now?" whispered Hans.

"You have to put a quarter in," said the woman, in a very unfriendly voice.

"Put a quarter in, Inge," said Hans.

"O.K.," said Inge, and then whispered to Hans, "I haven't got a quarter. You wait here and put in the soap and stuff, and I'll go and look for Mom." She dashed out of the laundromat door.

Hans had watched his mother putting the soap in lots of times. She used a cup. He found one and filled it up. The woman was still glaring.

Hans wondered how much soap to put in, but didn't want to ask the woman. So he dumped the whole cup in. Still the woman stood there, so Hans poured all the soap that was left in the box into the machine. The woman muttered, but didn't move. Hans smiled at her with his monster teeth.

The woman jumped and turned away. "That worked," thought Hans. "Now if Inge and Mom will just get back here with the quarter."

"There's a dryer stopped over here," Hans heard Mr. King yell. "Whose is it?" He was holding up a striped pyjama bottom.

Hans recognized it. "Oh, those are my dad's," he said. Everybody in the whole laundromat stopped and looked at Hans, and some of them laughed.

"Want to come and empty the dryer so someone else can use it?" Mr. King asked.

Hans found an empty basket and started to take out the dry clothes. They were hot! At last he got them all in the

basket and shoved it under the table where it would be out
of the way. There was no sign of Inge and his mother.

"See my car! See my car!"

Hans turned around and saw the baby who had been
crying earlier. She had dragged the Bergman's laundry
basket out from under the table and was pulling their clean
clothes onto the dirty laundromat floor.

"You stop that!" Hans shouted. He made a dive for the
baby.

She screamed and held on to the sides of the laundry
basket with all her might.

"What are you doing to my baby?" The woman who
had been waiting for the washing machine swooped down
on Hans. She was furious. She grabbed the screaming baby.

Mr. King came hurrying over.

"This boy," said the angry woman, "is bothering my baby and has a load of wash in a machine without any money to start it!"

Mr. King looked at Hans.

"My mom's bringing some change, and I've got the soap in," said Hans.

"Got the soap in, have you?" said Mr. King. "Well, then, suppose we just start it up, and you can give me the money when your mother gets back." He put a quarter in, the red light went on, and Hans heard the water rush into the machine.

Hans was trying to brush the footprints off his father's best shirt when he heard someone shout, "The soap! Look at the soap!"

All the soap Hans had poured into the washer had gone wild. Bubbles were pouring out of the washing machine, down the front, and onto the floor.

Hans forgot his father's shirt and rushed to the machine. He opened the lid, and a waterfall of suds gushed over him from head to foot. Suds piled up around the machine, and rivers of soap flowed across the floor.

Just then, Hans's father arrived back at the laundromat. There was poor Mr. King, trying to sweep the bubbles up with his broom; Hans, covered in soap suds, and a furious woman yelling at him. And there, right in the middle of the floor, was the baby in their laundry basket.

Hans had never been so glad to see his father in his life. And then his mother and Inge arrived.

"We had to walk three blocks to get change," said his mother.

"The garage was too busy to change my tires," said his father.

"I shouldn't have left you all by yourself," said Inge.

"I guess I put in a little too much soap," said Hans, and *everybody* laughed—even the woman with the baby.

Rules

BY KARLA KUSKIN

Do not jump on ancient uncles.

Do not yell at average mice.

Do not wear a broom to breakfast.

Do not ask a snake's advice.

Do not bathe in chocolate pudding.

Do not talk to bearded bears.

Do not snore on satin sofas.

Do not dance on velvet chairs.

Do not take a whale to visit
Russell's mother's cousin's yacht.

And whatever else you do do
It is better you
Do not.

News Items

Cougar prowls new subdivision

Port Moody, BC—There's a cougar prowling the edges of a new subdivision where the houses border a heavily treed hill.

Three people have reported seeing cougars in their backyards. One resident said a cougar came within three metres of him. Yesterday a cougar wandered through the busy intersection at Ioco and April Roads, bringing the traffic to a sudden stop.

Several house cats are missing in the neighborhood.

A provincial wildlife officer said that is a good indication of a cougar.

The wildlife officer with a pack of cougar hounds searched the area Wednesday but turned up nothing. He will search again when another sighting of a cougar is reported.

Parents in the area are nervous. They are keeping their children close to home, and are not letting them go into the woods to play. Pet owners are also keeping a close watch on their cats and dogs.

Bee swarms coaxed from neighborhood

New Minas, NS—The Burt family on Evergreen Street thought they were being invaded yesterday. A swarm of bees was hovering over the patio at the back of the house.

"We thought we were in a horror movie," said nine-year-old Ann Burt.

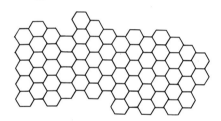

Mr. Burt called the police who soon arrived with John Hill, a beekeeper. Mr. Hill put on protective clothing and climbed up to the roof of the house. He placed a wax comb in a box to attract the bees. Within a short time the swarm had settled on the comb and Mr. Hill was able to take the bees away.

But Mr. Hill's services were soon in demand at another house a block away. Another swarm of bees was hovering over Lillian James' garden. This swarm included about 30,000 bees. The bees gave Mrs. James a scare.

"I closed all the windows and doors. I was afraid to put the garbage out," she said.

The bees likely came from the same source, Hill said, adding that a beekeeper in the area may have had an overcrowded hive. The bees are not dangerous, he said.

Hill thinks that the bees would have disappeared within a few hours or the next day—but people tend to panic.

Hill said he would be giving the bees to a farmer outside of town who wants more bees for his hives.

The Skunk on Yonge Street

BY SHARON SIAMON

The little policeman stamped his feet and waved a warning flag.

Scre-e-e-ch! All the traffic on four streets came to a sudden stop.

The air brakes on a big truck groaned and complained. The truck driver sat high up in the cab and scratched his head. He could see the green light up ahead at the intersection. So what was the problem? Why weren't the cars moving? His load had to be at the warehouse in a few minutes, and he didn't like being late.

Behind the truck was a tiny white sports car. The driver slammed on the brakes just in time to avoid running underneath the truck's big trailer. The driver looked up at the tall buildings all around and felt as small as an ant on a playground. What a place to be stuck in a traffic jam! What was happening up ahead anyway?

On another street that led into the jammed intersection was a long, grey limousine. Inside the car, the mayor was getting worried.

"I'll be late! I'll be late for lunch with the Queen! Somebody find out what's happening up there!"

Furiously the mayor punched buttons on his two-way radio to City Hall.

"This is the mayor speaking! Get the traffic controller! Check the traffic at the intersection of Yonge and St. Clair! Get it moving! I'm going to be late for the Queen's lunch!"

But in the middle of the intersection nothing moved. Not a car. Not a bus. Not a truck. Not a bicycle. Traffic lights blinked. Green-yellow-red. Green-yellow-red. And not a single driver stepped on the gas. Not a single person stepped into the crosswalk. No one in the intersection made a sound.

Further back on the four streets, horns blew and brakes squealed. But at the front of the traffic jam, the little policeman held all the people and all the cars as if they were under a magic spell. While he stood there, right in the middle of the intersection, no one was going anywhere.

For the little policeman was a skunk with two long white stripes running right down his back from his head to his tail. The night before, he had wandered up into the city centre from the shady ravine where he lived. He had made his way behind buildings and through alleys and finally stepped out from behind the bank on the corner—right into the rush-hour traffic.

He didn't hurry, and he didn't worry about people or cars. Skunks are like that. He knew all he had to do was stamp his feet and raise his tail like a warning flag and everyone would get out of his way. So he waved his tail and stamped around in a circle, and all the big trucks and busy people in Toronto couldn't make him hurry.

By now the mayor was talking to the pilot of the traffic helicopter on his two-way radio.

"Get the 'copter over here and get that traffic moving!" screeched the mayor. He was used to having his orders obeyed faster than this. Why couldn't they get things moving? At last the helicopter was coming. Now something would happen!

The traffic jam looked bad to the helicopter pilot. Blocks of stopped cars, trucks, streetcars, and buses tangled up like a big knot. But the intersection looked empty. She could see the traffic lights blinking—green, yellow, red—green, yellow, red. But nothing moved.

"Sorry, Mr. Mayor," the pilot said. "I can't see what the trouble is. The traffic lights are working, but no one is moving."

"Well, get down for a closer look! Land if you have to! But get me moving!" shouted the mayor.

"Yes, sir!" The pilot carefully circled lower.

She knew it was going to be dangerous and difficult to go down among the tall buildings, but the mayor had ordered it. So down she went.

At one hundred and fifty metres she could see a small black dot in the middle of the intersection.

At ninety metres, she called the mayor in his limousine.

"Sir, there's some little black thing moving down there. It seems to be causing the holdup. But just a minute! All the people are waving me away! They want me to take the 'copter up! I can see a policeman on the northeast corner! He's telling me to clear out! I'm going up, sir!" Carefully the pilot rose until the helicopter was clear of the tops of the buildings.

Down below, everyone waited. Nobody moved. The skunk's tail was straight up like a stick. He had been annoyed by the wind and the noise of that helicopter. He hadn't liked that one bit! But the noise disappeared, and slowly, slowly, his tail went down.

The little skunk would have liked to continue his walk, but there didn't seem to be any way out of the square. And the cars and the people were all jammed together. They didn't dare move forward and they couldn't move back. Things might have stayed that way if it hadn't been for the mayor.

He was getting angrier every minute. "It must be a bomb," he said. "Or maybe something from outer space. It has to be serious to make everyone stand like dummies."

So he picked up his radio again. "This is the mayor. Send the Special Emergency Squad to the intersection of Yonge and St. Clair! Immediately!"

While all this was going on, the skunk was getting tired of his adventure. He didn't like the hot pavement. And there was nothing to eat in the intersection—just some old popcorn that made him thirsty. He wanted to find his way back to the ravine for a snack.

The skunk didn't know he'd caused a traffic jam that stretched for blocks. He didn't know that the Emergency Squad and the bomb experts were on their way. He just felt like going on his way.

But he wasn't in a hurry. Skunks are never in a hurry. It's people who often are. And the hundreds of people in that traffic jam wanted to hurry. The mayor was in the biggest hurry of all. Finally he couldn't stand waiting any longer. He got out of his limousine and pushed through the crowd.

"Make way for the mayor! Make way for the mayor!" he shouted.

The skunk heard the commotion and turned toward it. He stamped his feet to show he was angry. People pressed back in alarm. But the mayor couldn't see what was happening. He just kept coming, pushing the people aside.

"Get out of the way! I'm the mayor!" he shouted.

The skunk's tail started to climb. It quivered with anger. The people held their breath—but the mayor kept pushing through the crowd.

"You people move aside! I'm the mayor of this city and. . ."

"Watch out, Mr. Mayor!" someone screamed, as the mayor pushed to the front and stood waving his arms and shouting.

The little skunk's tail shot straight up like a flag. Quick as lightning he whirled and shot the spray with deadly aim— right at the mayor.

"O-o-o-oh!" A cry went up from the crowd, as they tried to push back from the mayor and the terrible smell.

No one noticed that the little striped skunk had spotted an alley beside the bank and had made a beeline for it. He was going back to his ravine to find a nice shady spot to have a quiet nap.

Yonge Street was no longer quiet. People shouted. Horns honked. Engines roared into life. The mayor was hurried into the van of the Special Emergency Squad.

The people remembered all the important things they had to do. The traffic started moving. The truck rolled off to its warehouse. The sports car zipped off around the corner.

At last the noise and excitement were over. Some people soon forgot about the skunk on Yonge Street. But not the people who lived or worked near St. Clair and Yonge. And certainly not the mayor.

the wonderful mouse

from
the tip
of his
nose a
mouse is
cute, he
is so small
and furry. and
wherever he goes it always
seems, he is in such a hurry.
he's always scampering
here and there, in and out of
holes always running
away from the
cat, who follows
him wherever he goes, most people hate mice
but i think they're cute, even though they
may make nests, in the toe of some old boot.
some mice are grey
and blackish, some are
very white. some are
brown and greyish
some are black as night,
a mouse is quite a clever chap
who'll do anything for cheese,
and into the smallest tiniest
hole, a mouse could possibly squeeze.
a lovable pet, a house pest, a mouse is both
of these, always taking people's food,
never saying "please".
sharp, bright teeth. and as hungry as a whale. from the tip of his nose to the end of his tail.

BY KAREN CROSSLEY, AGE 11

Roundup in Stanley Park

BY ANN IRWIN

You may have heard of a cattle roundup, or a roundup of wild horses long ago in the west. But did you know that in Stanley Park, Vancouver every year there's a wild goose roundup?

There are too many wild Canada Geese around Lost Lagoon in Stanley Park. So each year the park staff try to round up some of the geese and move them to other places. They start by herding the geese to shore with rowboats. No horses for these cowboys!

Once the geese are all on shore, two lines of volunteers make a long pathway to the tennis courts.

Tennis anyone? Some of the big birds are not too happy about being herded into the courts, but they don't need to worry. They won't be harmed.

It's a little crowded once all the geese are safely rounded up. And more than a little bit noisy!

The last step in the wild goose roundup is loading the geese into poultry trucks. Then they'll be driven to areas where there are not so many geese and they can spread out once more.

Lost Lagoon is once more a peaceful place. A few geese are left for park visitors to enjoy. Next year, there'll be another wild goose roundup.

Whose House Is This, Anyway?

BY SHEILA DALTON

On the day we got back to Vancouver from our vacation, we were in my mom's bedroom unpacking when we heard a loud HONK!

"What was *that*?" said Mom, turning around.

"I don't know," said Gramps. He walked from the bedroom to the living room. There was a short silence, followed by another loud HONK. "But it *could* be the Canada Goose on the balcony."

"Canada Goose! On the balcony!" cried Mom. And she dropped an armful of dirty towels and ran to look. My brother and I followed right behind. Sure enough, there on the balcony in amongst the flowerpots and lawn chairs and a whole bunch of other junk were not one, but two, Canada Geese.

"What on earth. . .," began my mother as she marched forward and slid the door open. She was cut short by a loud HISSSSS and a mad flapping of wings. SLAM went the door.

"That must be the male goose," said Gramps. "There must be eggs in there. They always stay with the female and defend the nest."

"NEST?" Mom was practically yelling by then.

It's not all *that* unusual for Canada Geese to build nests on apartment balconies in Vancouver, but it had never happened in our building before. Mom looked really upset.

"How are we going to get rid of them?" she said staring out at the two big birds with their long black necks and white cheeks. The female was sitting on top of a tangled heap of twigs and sticks—and what looked a lot like a pair of Mom's gardening gloves. The male was still stalking around with its neck stretched out and its wings open.

"Oh, please, can't they stay? At least until the eggs hatch?" I pleaded. I love Canada Geese, and I could hardly wait to see the baby birds when they came out of their shells.

But Mom said that the Superintendent would never allow it. Then she remembered he had gone on vacation, too. He wouldn't be back for at least two weeks.

She and Gramps were just starting to talk about what to do, when Jamie remembered he'd promised to go biking with his friend Rob as soon as he got home.

Without thinking, he opened the balcony door and stepped outside to get his ten-speed.

Well, that gander rushed right at him with its big beak wide open. It was making the most awful SSSSing noise, sort of like a giant snake. My brother backed up fast and crashed into a pot full of pansies. The goose reached out with its beak and grabbed a piece of Jamie's favorite robot tee-shirt. Jamie backed up. The goose held on. RRRRRRRIPP!

Have you ever seen a Canada Goose with a picture of a robot dangling from its mouth? I couldn't help laughing.

"Say, whose house is this, anyway?" cried Jamie angrily. Mom grabbed my brother's arm and pulled him back into the apartment.

Mom and Gramps were *still* trying to decide what to do, when the gander flew off. But Jamie was too shook up to go out on the balcony right away. "Just a minute," he said when Mom tried to shoo him out there. Then he went and locked himself in the bathroom.

When he came out he had big black rings around his eyes and little whiskers sprouting all around his nose. Gramps took one look at him and started laughing so hard he couldn't catch his breath. I had to thump him on the back and get him a glass of water.

Mom wasn't laughing, though. "If that's my mascara all over your face, Jamie Westcott," she said in a voice that sounded like a stretched rubber band, "you'd better start saving your allowance to get me some more *right now*."

Jamie blushed (you could see his face getting red around the black rings) and said, " I read at school that Canada Geese are afraid of raccoons. I'm dressing up as a raccoon, to scare that rotten old gander if he comes back too soon."

I had to get Gramps another glass of water.

Gramps ended up getting Jamie's bike for him, and things settled down to normal. Sort of. While Mom and Gramps were discussing what to do, the gander came back.

The more the grown-ups talked, the more the geese "talked" too. They honked and gabbled and even hissed once in a while. They made quite a racket.

Mom was all for calling the Humane Society right away, but they were closed on Sundays. So she said she'd do it first thing the next day.

In the morning, the geese were really quiet, and I caught Mom gazing out at them through the kitchen window.

"You know," she said when I came in. "Those geese *are* beautiful, and they're really intelligent. When I was a little girl, my mother used to take me to the park behind our house so we could watch them on the river. It got so they recognized us, and would greet us when we came."

"So you'll let them stay?" I asked hopefully.

"Not so fast," Mom said. "Even if I don't mind having them here, I'm not so sure about your brother or your grandfather. Not to mention the other tenants, and the Superintendent when he gets back."

Well, I knew I could persuade Gramps pretty easily. He'd already told me *his* childhood memories of geese flying over his parents' farm. But Jamie was another matter.

That morning he'd taped a picture of a fox on the glass balcony door. He'd faced it outwards so the geese would see it. Foxes eat goose eggs. In the afternoon, I caught him howling like a coyote through the screen. Coyotes eat geese.

It seems he just couldn't get over that gander ripping his favorite shirt. And I knew as long as Jamie made a fuss, Mom would get rid of the geese.

It was Mrs. Archer, of all people, who made Jamie change his mind. Mrs. Archer lives in the apartment below us. She's always mad at Jamie and I about something. Mom says she acts like that because she's lonely. I say it's no wonder she doesn't have any company.

She pounded on our door that afternoon like there was a whole army chasing her. When Mom opened it Mrs. Archer barged in and started shouting. She didn't even wait to take off her silly hat with the red cherries on it.

"So you're back at last," she fumed, while the cherries on her hat went bob, bob, bob. "I've had sticks and stones and who knows what else falling on my balcony for two weeks now. And the noise! If your son doesn't get rid of his pet geese soon, I'll get rid of them for him!"

"They're not *my* pet geese," said Jamie. "I hate them."

Before anyone could stop her, Mrs. Archer marched out onto the balcony. I couldn't watch. The shouting and hissing was terrible.

There wasn't much left of Mrs. Archer's hat when she came back in. But for some reason she didn't seem so angry.

"There are eggs in that nest!" she said in a surprised voice. "Just think! Canada Geese choosing *our* building for nesting."

Jamie stared at her. I didn't blame him. Mrs. Archer sure seemed different now that she knew about the eggs. She must have noticed Jamie staring because her face got red and she said, "I guess I made a mistake, Jamie. I love animals and I thought you'd caught those geese and wouldn't let them go. I'm sorry."

Jamie looked really pleased. I think he decided right then that Mrs. Archer and the geese weren't so bad after all, because he turned to Mom and asked if we could let the geese stay.

Mom and Gramps agreed to wait at least until the Superintendent got back before they called the Humane Society. Two days before he did, the eggs hatched.

Mrs. Archer was over visiting when it happened. She'd been coming to our apartment so often to see how the geese were doing that she was almost like family by then. It was hard to remember how awful I used to think she was. Especially when she took one look at those four fluffy goslings and reached over and gave me a hug. "Patsy, dear," she said, "this is one of the nicest times I've had in ages."

Who can stay mad at someone as friendly as that?

Raccoon

BY WAYNE PICHETTE

A raccoon
stopped to play
on the lawn outside
my 20-storey apartment building.
    What raccoon in her right mind
would play
in such a smoggy place of the city,
on such a dismal day?
    Horns beep and tires squeal.
She does not
move far away
from the nearest tree, her safety.
    I would like to tell her
to gather up her children
and leave this city
as quickly as possible.
    You see, it seems to me
that a smoggy city
is no place
for raccoons.

160